C000078964

# STARGAZING 2012

## MONTH-BY-MONTH GUIDE TO THE NORTHERN NIGHT SKY

# HEATHER COUPER & NIGEL HENBEST

www.philips-maps.co.uk

HEATHER COUPER and NIGEL HENBEST are inter-
nationally recognized writers and broadcasters on
astronomy, space and science. They have written more
than 30 books and over 1000 articles, and are the
founders of an independent TV production company
specializing in factual and scientific programming.

Heather is a past President of both the British
Astronomical Association and the Society for Popular
Astronomy. She is a Fellow of the Royal Astronomical
Society, a Fellow of the Institute of Physics and a former
Millennium Commissioner, for which she was awarded
the CBE in 2007. Nigel has been Astronomy Consultant
to *New Scientist* magazine, Editor of the *Journal of the
British Astronomical Association* and Media Consultant to
the Royal Greenwich Observatory.

Published in Great Britain in 2011
by Philip's,
a division of Octopus Publishing Group Limited
(www.octopusbooks.co.uk)
Endeavour House, 189 Shaftesbury Avenue,
London WC2H 8JY
An Hachette UK Company (www.hachette.co.uk)

Reprinted 2012

**TEXT**
Heather Couper and Nigel Henbest (pages 6–53)
Robin Scagell (pages 61–64)
Philip's (pages 1–5, 54–60)

Copyright © 2011 Heather Couper and Nigel Henbest
(pages 6–53)

Copyright © 2011 Philip's (pages 1–5, 54–64)

ISBN 978–1–84907–175–8

Printed in China

Title page: *Rosette Nebula (Gordon Rogers/Galaxy)*

**ACKNOWLEDGEMENTS**
All star maps by Wil Tirion/Philip's,
with extra annotation by Philip's.
Artworks © Philip's.

**All photographs courtesy of
Galaxy Picture Library:**
Paul Andrew *12;*
Howard Brown-Greaves *48;*
Jamie Cooper *24, 28;*
David Hepwood *52;*
Damian Peach *16, 40;*
Gordon Rogers *8;*
Robin Scagell *20, 36, 61–64;*
Peter Shah *44;*
Michael Stecker *33.*

# CONTENTS

The sight of diamond-bright stars sparkling against a sky of black velvet is one of life's most glorious experiences. No wonder stargazing is so popular. Learning your way around the night sky requires nothing more than patience, a reasonably clear sky and the 12 star charts included in this book.

Stargazing 2012 is a guide to the sky for every month of the year. Complete beginners will use it as an essential night-time companion, while seasoned amateur astronomers will find the updates invaluable.

## THE MONTHLY CHARTS

Each pair of monthly charts shows the views of the heavens looking north and south. They are usable throughout most of Europe – between 40 and 60 degrees north. Only the brightest stars are shown (otherwise we would have had to put 3000 stars on each chart, instead of about 200). This means that we plot stars down to third magnitude, with a few fourth-magnitude stars to complete distinctive patterns. We also show the ecliptic, which is the apparent path of the Sun in the sky.

## USING THE STAR CHARTS

To use the charts, begin by locating the north Pole Star – Polaris – by using the stars of the Plough (see May). When you are looking at Polaris you are facing north, with west on your left and east on your right. (West and east are reversed on star charts because they show the view looking up into the sky instead of down towards the ground.) The left-hand chart then shows the view you have to the north. Most of the stars you see will be circumpolar, which means that they are visible all year. The other stars rise in the east and set in the west.

Now turn and face the opposite direction, south. This is the view that changes most during the course of the year. Leo, with its prominent 'sickle' formation, is high in the spring skies. Summer is dominated by the bright trio of Vega, Deneb and Altair. Autumn's familiar marker is the Square of Pegasus, while the winter sky is ruled over by the stars of Orion.

The charts show the sky as it appears in the late evening for each month: the exact times are noted in the caption with the chart. If you are observing in the early morning, you will find that the view is different. As a rule of thumb, if you are observing two hours later than the time suggested in the caption, then the following month's map will more accurately represent the stars on view. So, if you wish to observe at midnight in the middle of February, two hours later than the time suggested in the caption, then the stars will appear as they are on March's chart. When using a chart for the 'wrong' month, however, bear in mind that the planets and Moon will not be shown in their correct positions.

### THE MOON, PLANETS AND SPECIAL EVENTS

In addition to the stars visible each month, the charts show the positions of any planets on view in the late evening. Other planets may also be visible that month, but they will not be on the chart if they have already set, or if they do not rise until early morning. Their positions are described in the text, so that you can find them if you are observing at other times.

We have also plotted the path of the Moon. Its position is marked at three-day intervals. The dates when it reaches First Quarter, Full Moon, Last Quarter and New Moon are given in the text. If there is a meteor shower in the month, we mark the position from which the meteors appear to emanate – the *radiant*. More information on observing the planets and other Solar System objects is given on pages 54–57.

Once you have identified the constellations and found the planets, you will want to know more about what's on view. Each month, we explain one object, such as a particularly interesting star or galaxy, in detail. We have also chosen a spectacular image for each month and described how it was captured. All of these pictures were taken by amateurs. We list details and dates of special events, such as meteor showers or eclipses, and give observing tips. Finally, each month we pick a topic related to what's on view, ranging from the Milky Way to star colours and light pollution, and discuss it in more detail. Where possible, all relevant objects are highlighted on the maps.

### FURTHER INFORMATION

The year's star charts form the heart of the book, providing material for many enjoyable observing sessions. For background information turn to pages 54–57, where diagrams help to explain, among other things, the movement of the planets and why we see eclipses.

Although there is plenty to see with the naked eye, many observers use binoculars or telescopes, and some choose to record their observations using cameras, CCDs or webcams. For a round-up of what's new in observing technology, go to pages 61–64, where equipment expert Robin Scagell shares his knowledge of safely observing the Sun.

If you have already invested in binoculars or a telescope, then you can explore the deep sky – nebulae (starbirth sites), star clusters and galaxies. On pages 58–60 we list recommended deep-sky objects, constellation by constellation. Use the appropriate month's maps to see which constellations are on view, and then choose your targets. The table of 'limiting magnitude' (page 58) will help you to decide if a particular object is visible with your equipment.

Happy stargazing!

Orion, **Taurus**, **Gemini** and **Canis Major** make up a scintillating celestial tableau in January, so there's no better time to start finding your way around the sky. And this year, the planets **Venus**, **Jupiter** and **Mars** add to the brilliant cast of characters.

▼ *The sky at 10 pm in mid-January, with Moon positions at three-day intervals either side of Full Moon. The star positions are also correct for 11 pm at*

### JANUARY'S CONSTELLATION

Spectacular **Orion** is one of the rare star-groupings that looks like its namesake – a giant of a man with a sword below his belt, wielding a club above his head. Orion is fabled in mythology as the ultimate hunter.

The constellation contains one-tenth of the brightest stars in the sky: its seven main stars all lie in the 'top 70' of brilliant stars. Despite its distinctive shape, most of these stars are not closely associated with each other – they simply line up, one behind the other.

Closest to us is the star that forms the hunter's right shoulder, **Bellatrix**, at 240 light years distance. Next is blood-red **Betelgeuse**, at the top left of Orion, 600 light years away.

The constellation's brightest star, blue-white **Rigel**, is a vigorous young star more than twice as hot as our Sun, and 50,000 times as bright. Rigel lies 800 light years from us, roughly the same distance as the star that marks the other corner of Orion's tunic – **Saiph** – and the two outer stars of the belt, **Alnitak** (left) and **Mintaka** (right).

We travel 1300 light years from home to reach the middle star of the belt, **Alnilam**. And at the same distance, we reach the stars of the 'sword' hanging below the belt – the lair of the great **Orion Nebula**.

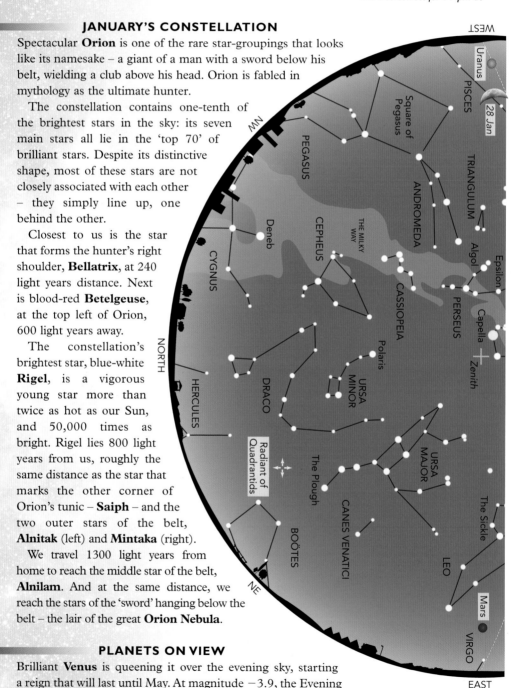

### PLANETS ON VIEW

Brilliant **Venus** is queening it over the evening sky, starting a reign that will last until May. At magnitude −3.9, the Evening

*the beginning of January, and 9 pm at the end of the month. The planets move slightly relative to the stars during the month.*

Star is setting three hours after the Sun, low in the south-west.

This month, Venus passes **Neptune**, which is spending the month in Aquarius and setting around 7.30 pm. With a small telescope, you can find Neptune just over a degree from Venus (above on 12 January and to the upper right on 13 January); at magnitude +8.0, the most distant planet is 60,000 times fainter than the Evening Star.

**Uranus**, lying in Pisces, is just visible to the naked eye at magnitude +5.9. It sets around 10.30 pm.

The later evening is **Jupiter**'s domain. The giant planet – perched on the border of Pisces and Aries – sets around 2.00 am at the beginning of January, and 0.20 am by the end of the month. Shining at magnitude −2.3, it's even more spectacular than any of the bright winter stars.

**Mars** brightens from magnitude +0.2 to −0.5 during January. Tucked under the tail of Leo, the Red Planet rises at 10 pm at the start of the month, and at 8.30 pm at the end of January.

It's followed by **Saturn** (magnitude +1.0), rising at around 1 am in Virgo.

In the first week of the year, you can catch **Mercury** low down in the south-east before sunrise, shining at magnitude −0.3.

## MOON

On 2 January, the Moon lies close to Jupiter. It's near Mars on the night of 13/14 January. On the morning of 16 January, the Last Quarter Moon passes below Spica, with Saturn to the

January's Picture
Rosette Nebula

Radiant of
Quadrantids

Mars
Jupiter
Uranus
Moon

| MOON | | |
|---|---|---|
| Date | Time | Phase |
| 1 | 6.15 am | First Quarter |
| 9 | 7.30 am | Full Moon |
| 16 | 9.08 am | Last Quarter |
| 23 | 7.39 am | New Moon |
| 31 | 4.10 am | First Quarter |

upper left; the Moon is below Saturn on the morning of 17 January. The waning crescent Moon rises above Antares on 19 January. The waxing crescent Moon forms a lovely sight with Venus after sunset on 26 January. And the bright planet near the Moon on 29 and 30 January is Jupiter.

## SPECIAL EVENTS

On **5 January**, the Earth is at perihelion, its closest point to the Sun.

The maximum of the **Quadrantid** meteor shower occurs on the night of **3/4 January**. These shooting stars are tiny particles of dust shed by the old comet 2003 $EH_1$, burning up as they enter the Earth's atmosphere. Best to look after 3.30 am, when the Moon has set.

## JANUARY'S OBJECT

**Venus** – the planet of love – is resplendent in our evening skies early this year. So brilliant and beautiful, she can even cast a shadow when skies are really dark and transparent. Her purity and lantern-like luminosity are beguiling – but looks are deceptive. Earth's twin in size, Venus could hardly be more different from our warm, wet world. The reason for the planet's brilliance is the result of the highly reflective clouds that cloak its surface: probe under these palls of sulphuric acid, and you find a planet out of hell. Volcanoes are to blame. They have belched out carbon dioxide to create a runaway 'greenhouse effect' that has made Venus the hottest and most poisonous planet in the Solar System. At 460°C, this world is hotter than an oven. The pressure at its surface is around 90 Earth atmospheres. So – if you visited Venus – you'd be simultaneously roasted, crushed, corroded and suffocated!

## JANUARY'S PICTURE

The beautiful **Rosette Nebula** is a celestial gem. Some 5000 light years away, the 'petals' of the rose spread out over 130 light years of space. Baby stars are being born in the nebula today, their violent radiation and powerful winds punching a hole in the nebula's heart. Astronomers believe that the Rosette is capable of giving birth to 10,000 stars.

## JANUARY'S TOPIC
### The Oort–Öpik Cloud

Everyone is thrilled with excitement when a new comet hoves into view. Who can ever forget the magnificence of Comet Hale-Bopp in 1997?

But – throughout history – comets have always had a dodgy reputation. As Shakespeare wrote in his play *Julius Caesar*: 'When beggars die, there are no comets seen. The heavens themselves blaze forth the death of princes.'

These interlopers into our heavens seem to appear out of nowhere. And – if they come close to the Earth – they can look like malevolent daggers hanging in the sky. It's no wonder that many people believed they were portents of disaster.

And their instincts were right. In 1908, a mysterious object – probably a comet – exploded in the skies above Tunguska, Siberia. The shockwave it created flattened forests and killed thousands of reindeer.

What are comets – and where do they come from? These 'dirty snowballs' are icy and rocky debris left over from the creation of the planets. As they sweep in towards the Sun, their ices boil, creating a massive head of gas and a trailing tail millions of kilometres long.

But, as well as causing destruction, these icy visitors may be the bringers of life. Many scientists believe that Earth's oceans were delivered to us from space by comets.

Today, millions of comets live in a huge sphere surrounding our Solar System, which extends almost a quarter of the way to the nearest star. The Oort-Öpik Cloud (named after the two astronomers who speculated upon its existence) is a repository of the building blocks of the planets. And when passing stars disturb the cloud, a new comet plunges into the inner Solar System, creating a glorious spectacle in our night skies.

◉ **Viewing tip**
Venus is a real treat this month. If you have a small telescope, though, don't wait for the sky to get really dark. Seen against a black sky, the cloud-wreathed planet is so brilliant that it's difficult to make out anything on its disc. Instead, view the planet as soon as it's visible in the twilight glow, and you can then see the globe of Venus appearing fainter against a pale blue sky.

The first signs of spring are now on the way, as the winter star-patterns start to drift towards the west, setting earlier. The constantly changing pageant of constellations in the sky is proof that we live on a cosmic merry-go-round, orbiting the Sun. Imagine that you're in the fairground, circling the Mighty Wurlitzer on your horse, and looking out around you. At times you spot the ghost train; sometimes you see the roller-coaster; and then you swing past the candy-floss stall. So it is with the sky – and the constellations – as we circle our local star. That's why we get to see different stars in different seasons.

## FEBRUARY'S CONSTELLATION

You can't ignore **Gemini** in February. High in the south, the constellation is dominated by the stars **Castor** and **Pollux**, which are of similar brightness and represent the heads of a pair of twins – their stellar bodies run in parallel lines of stars towards the west. Legend has it that Castor and Pollux were twins, conceived on the same night by the princess Leda. On the night she married the king of Sparta, wicked old Zeus (Jupiter) also invaded the marital suite, disguised as a swan. Pollux was the result of the liaison with Jupiter – and therefore immortal – while Castor was merely a human being. But the pair were so devoted to each other that Zeus decided to grant Castor honorary immortality, and placed both him and Pollux amongst the stars.

Castor, as it turns out, is an amazing star. It's actually not just one star, but a family of six. Even through a small telescope, you can see that Castor is a double star, comprising two stars circling each other. Both of these are double (although you need special equipment to detect this). Then there's another outlying star, visible through a telescope, which also turns out to be double.

▼ *The sky at 10 pm in mid-February, with Moon positions at three-day intervals either side of Full Moon. The star positions are also correct for 11 pm at the beginning of February, and 9 pm at the end of the month. The planets move slightly relative to the stars during the month.*

## PLANETS ON VIEW

**Venus** continues to brighten as the Evening Star moves towards the Earth, reaching magnitude −4.1 by the close of February. The planet's bedtime grows steadily later, from 8.30 pm to 10.00 pm by month's end.

On 9 February, Venus passes close by **Uranus**, providing a fine opportunity to locate this dim world. When the sky is dark, but before Venus is too low, find the planet in binoculars and look half a degree to the left to spot Uranus. The penultimate planet is 10,000 times fainter than Venus, at magnitude +5.9; it's currently residing in Pisces and sets about 8.30 pm.

**Jupiter**, in Aries, is gradually fading as Earth pulls away – but it still outshines all the stars, at magnitude −2.2. The giant planet is setting at 0.20 am at the start of the month, and just before 11 pm by the end of February.

Watch **Mars** to see how it brightens astonishingly this month, ahead of its closest approach to Earth in March: the Red Planet doubles in brilliance, from magnitude −0.5 to −1.2. Lying under Leo, Mars rises at 8.20 pm at the beginning of February, and at 5.40 pm by month's end.

**Saturn** lies in Virgo, rising just before midnight at the start of the month, and at 10 pm by the close of February. The ringworld shines at magnitude +0.8.

On the last couple of evenings of February, you may just catch **Mercury** (magnitude −0.8) very low in the west after sunset; it will be better early next month!

WEST

PISCES
CETUS
PERSEUS
Pleiades
TAURUS
ERIDANUS
Aldebaran
LEPUS
Rigel
1 Feb
Zenith
Capella
AURIGA
GEMINI
Castor
Pollux
4 Feb
Betelgeuse
ORION
Sirius
CANIS MAJOR
Adhara
Procyon
CANIS MINOR
THE MILKY WAY
SOUTH
URSA MAJOR
The Sickle
CANCER
7 Feb
PUPPIS
Regulus
HYDRA
LEO
Mars
VIRGO
10 Feb
Ecliptic
EAST
SW
SE

| | Mars |
| | Jupiter |
| | Moon |

February's Object
Sirius

| **MOON** | | |
|---|---|---|
| **Date** | **Time** | **Phase** |
| 7 | 9.54 pm | Full Moon |
| 14 | 5.04 pm | Last Quarter |
| 21 | 10.35 pm | New Moon |

**Neptune** is too close to the Sun to be visible this month.

## MOON

On 3 February, the Moon occults the Crab Nebula (see Special Events). The Moon passes below Regulus on 8 February, and Mars on the night of 9/10 February. On 12/13 February, the Moon lies below Saturn, with Spica to the Moon's upper right. Before dawn on 15 February, you'll find the Last Quarter Moon near Antares. Dusk on 25 February sees the crescent Moon very close to Venus – a glorious sight – with Jupiter above. And on 26 February, the Moon lies near Jupiter, with brilliant Venus below.

## SPECIAL EVENTS

On **3 February**, the Moon occults the Crab Nebula (a fascinating challenge if you have a moderate telescope) as seen from the southern parts of the UK – and better from Europe. The dark edge of the Moon starts to hide the supernova remnant at 6.05 pm, and it re-emerges by 6.50 pm.

Also on **3 February**, NASA plans to launch NuSTAR, a ground-breaking mission to search for the most extreme results of violence in the Universe. It will sniff out black holes; map the gruesome results of supernova explosions; and study the most devastating effects of exploding galaxies.

▲ *Paul Andrew captured this beautiful picture of the Aurora Borealis at Dover, Kent, on 29 October 2003. He used a Canon 10D with a 15 mm lens at f/5.6, and a 30-second exposure at ISO 800.*

## FEBRUARY'S OBJECT

This is the month of the brightest star in the sky – **Sirius**. It isn't a particularly luminous star: it just happens to lie nearby, at a distance of 8.6 light years. The 'Dog Star' is accompanied

**Viewing tip**

It may sound obvious, but if you want to stargaze at this most glorious time of year, dress up warmly! Lots of layers are better than a heavy coat as they trap air next to your skin – and heavy-soled boots stop the frost creeping up your legs. It may sound anorakish, but a woolly hat really does stop one-third of your body's heat escaping through the top of your head. And, alas, no hipflask of whisky – alcohol constricts the veins and will make you feel even colder.

by a little companion, affectionately called 'The Pup'. This tiny star was discovered in 1862 by Alvan Clark when he was testing a telescope; but it had been predicted by Friedrich Bessel nearly 20 years before, when he'd observed that something was 'tugging' on Sirius. The Pup is a white dwarf: the dying nuclear reactor of an ancient star that has puffed off its atmosphere. White dwarfs are the size of a planet but have the mass of a star: because they're so collapsed, they have considerable gravitational powers – hence Sirius' wobble. The Pup is visible through medium-powered telescopes.

## FEBRUARY'S PICTURE

As solar activity continues to hot up – as part of our local star's 11-year magnetic cycle – look out for the Northern Lights. The **Aurora Borealis** is caused when energetic electrical particles from the Sun hit the Earth's magnetic poles. The result: a neon glow in the sky, and a glorious light-show of shifting curtains and rays. Although aurorae are normally restricted to high northern latitudes, very powerful displays can be seen further south.

## FEBRUARY'S TOPIC
### Leap year

This year, February is blessed with an extra day (as anyone born on 29 February is all too aware!), making 2012 a 'leap year'. We have leap years because there aren't an exact number of days in a year: in fact, a year is 365.2422 days long. Julius Caesar declared that every fourth year should have an extra day (added to poor February, as it's the shortest month). That makes an average of 365.25 days per year – which still isn't quite right. In 1582, Pope Gregory XIII changed the rules, so that a century year is a leap year only if you can divide it by 400. So 2000 was a leap year, while 2100 won't be. Over many centuries, the 'Gregorian calendar year' averages out to 365.2425 days. That's pretty close to the actual length of the year. But, amazingly, back in AD 1079, the Persian astronomer and poet Omar Khayyam devised a calendar with a pattern of eight leap years spread over a 33-year period, and this calendar – still used in Iran – averages to 365.2424 days per year, which is more accurate than our Gregorian calendar!

This month is a veritable planet-gazer's paradise: all five naked-eye planets are on view before midnight, with Mercury, Venus and Mars each putting on their best evening performance of the year.

Also this month, the nights become shorter than the days as we hit the Vernal Equinox – on 20 March, spring is 'official'. That's the date when the Sun climbs up over the equator to shed its rays over the northern hemisphere. Because of the Earth's inclination of 23.5° to its orbital path around the Sun, the North Pole points away from our local star between September and March, causing the long nights of autumn and winter. Come the northern spring, Earth's axial tilt favours the Sun – and we can look forward to the long, warm days of summer.

Even better, the clocks 'spring forward' on 25 March, so nightfall comes even later.

### MARCH'S CONSTELLATION

Now sinking in the western evening skies, the diminutive constellation of **Canis Minor** faithfully follows its larger companion **Canis Major** – dominated by the brilliant star **Sirius** – towards the horizon. Consisting of just two stars, the 'Little Dog' is hardly the most spectacular constellation. Yet its chief star – **Procyon** – is the seventh brightest in the sky. Its name translates to 'before the dog', because in northern latitudes it rises before the Dog Star, Sirius.

Procyon is a white star, 7.5 times more luminous than the Sun. Like Sirius (see February's Object), it is orbited by a tiny white dwarf star, which is hard to pick out even in large telescopes.

The other star in the constellation – **Gomeisa** – spins rapidly and is slightly variable. In Arabic, its name means 'the bleary-eyed woman'. Gomeisa is surrounded by a disc of cosmic dust, which is currently heating up – possibly a planetary system in the process of being born.

▼ The sky at 10 pm in mid-March, with Moon positions at three-day intervals either side of Full Moon. The star positions are also correct for 11 pm at *the beginning of March, and 10 pm at the end of the month (after BST begins). The planets move slightly relative to the stars during the month.*

## PLANETS ON VIEW

In the first half of March, look west after sunset to catch elusive **Mercury**, putting on its best evening show of the year. The innermost planet is setting about an hour and three-quarters after the Sun, and reaches its greatest eastern elongation on 5 March. It's easiest to spot Mercury at the start of the month, when the planet is at magnitude −0.8; by 12 March it has faded to magnitude +1.2.

Higher in the west, brilliant **Venus** blazes all month long. At greatest elongation on 27 March, the Evening Star is setting after midnight, an amazing 4 hours 40 minutes later than the Sun. The moonless evenings just after mid-month are an ideal time to check for shadows cast by the magnitude −4.2 planet.

Forming a spectacular double act with Venus in the evening sky is the second-brightest planet, **Jupiter**: the Evening Star passes the giant planet on 13 March. Jupiter, at magnitude −2.0, is eight times fainter than Venus. Jupiter lies in Aries all month, setting at 10.50 pm at the beginning of March, and at 10.30 pm by the end of the month.

For all the excitement we've seen so far, **Mars** is the true planetary star of the month, reaching its two-yearly opposition on 3 March. Lying in Leo, Mars is visible all night long. At opposition, it is magnitude −1.2 (making the Red Planet just a little fainter than the brightest star, Sirius), but it fades to magnitude −0.8 by the end of March.

WEST

EAST

| | MOON | | |
|---|---|---|---|
| | **Date** | **Time** | **Phase** |
| | 1 | 1.22 am | First Quarter |
| | 8 | 9.39 am | Full Moon |
| | 15 | 1.25 am | Last Quarter |
| | 22 | 2.37 pm | New Moon |
| | 30 | 8.41 pm | First Quarter |

Venus
Mars
Jupiter
Saturn
Moon

March's Object and Picture Mars

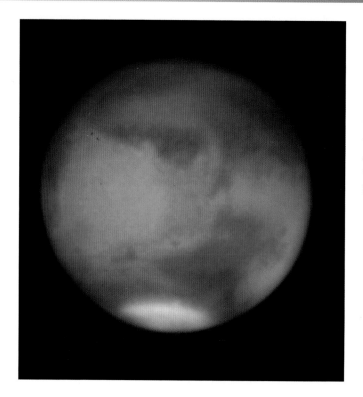

◄ On 31 January 2010, Damian Peach took this picture of Mars from High Wycombe, Buckinghamshire. He used a Celestron C14 (355 mm) Schmidt-Cassegrain telescope with a Lumenera SKYnyx camera, equipped with red, green and blue filters. Each separate image was compiled from a video sequence.

Bringing up the rear of this amazing planetary parade is **Saturn**, rising around 10 pm at the beginning of March, and by 9 pm at month's end. Lying in Virgo, Saturn – at magnitude +0.6 – is slightly brighter than the constellation's principal star, Spica.

**Uranus** and **Neptune** are lost in the Sun's glare in March.

## MOON

On 6 March, the Moon lies near Regulus. The Full Moon passes below Mars on the night of 7/8 March, and you'll find the Moon below Spica and Saturn on the night of 10/11 March. Antares is the star to the right of the Moon in the early hours of 14 March. On 25 March, the crescent Moon is just to the right of Jupiter, with brilliant Venus above; the next night (26 March) the roles are reversed, with Venus just to the right of the Moon, and Jupiter below.

## SPECIAL EVENTS

The Vernal Equinox, on **20 March** at 5.14 am, marks the beginning of spring, as the Sun moves up to shine over the northern hemisphere.

**25 March**, 1.00 am: British Summer Time starts – don't forget to put your clocks forward by an hour (the mnemonic is '*Spring* forward, *Fall* back').

## MARCH'S OBJECT

On 3 March, **Mars** is at opposition, though its elliptical orbit means the Red Planet is actually closest to Earth – 101 million kilometres – two days later. Use a small telescope to skim over its mottled surface, and spot its icy polar caps.

The debate about ice, water and life on Mars has hotted up over the last few years. There's evidence from NASA's Viking landings in 1976 that primitive bacterial life was then still in existence. And the present flotilla of space probes, which are crawling over its surface or orbiting the Red Planet, are unanimously picking up evidence for present or past water all over Mars – the essential ingredient for life.

If all goes according to plan, NASA's Curiosity mission should now be on its way to the Red Planet. Its rover – the size of a Mini-Cooper car – will investigate the geology, composition and life-potential of the Red Planet. And for the first time, NASA admits it has designed the project with a view that looks at the possibility of humans going to Mars.

## MARCH'S PICTURE

**Mars** certainly deserves a photo-opportunity this month. The Red Planet is the most Earth-like world in the Solar System, with its polar caps, volcanoes and thin atmosphere. This image shows the northern polar cap well (telescope images are traditionally inverted), as well as some of the dark rocky outcrops on Mars. The prominent triangular Syrtis Major is on the far left, covered by blue cloud; just above the centre is Sinus Meridiani.

## MARCH'S TOPIC
### Cosmic blasts

Asteroids and meteorites – friend or foe? These small chunks of rock and iron built up the planets of our Solar System. Most of these building blocks have been incorporated into worlds, but some debris remains and now it poses a threat. About 65 million years ago, an asteroid some 10 kilometres across struck the Yucatan Peninsula in Central America – leading to worldwide devastation that wiped out all the higher forms of life, including the dinosaurs. Astronomers are aware that Earth's orbit is crisscrossed by over 1000 potentially hazardous asteroids. To avoid cosmic disaster in the future, researchers are pinpointing their positions – and devising strategies to blast them off collision course.

The ancient constellations of **Leo** and **Virgo** dominate the springtime skies. Leo does indeed look like a recumbent lion, but it's hard to envisage Virgo as anything other than a vast 'Y' in the sky!

When you're looking at Virgo, spot the interloper. It's the planet Saturn, closest to the Earth this month. 'Close', however, is relative: the ringworld is over a billion kilometres distant. Nearer – and more spectacular – is brilliant Venus: the Evening Star hangs like a tiny lantern in the west after sunset.

### APRIL'S CONSTELLATION

Like the mighty hunter Orion, **Leo** is one of the rare constellations that looks like its namesake – in this case, an enormous crouching lion. Leo is one of the oldest constellations, and commemorates the giant Nemean lion that Hercules slaughtered as the first of his labours. According to legend, the lion's flesh could not be pierced by iron, stone or bronze – so Hercules wrestled with the lion and choked it to death.

The lion's heart is marked by the first-magnitude star **Regulus**, and its other end by **Denebola**, which in Arabic means 'the lion's tail'. A small telescope shows that **Algieba**, the star marking the lion's shoulder, is actually a beautiful close double star. Just underneath the main 'body' of Leo are several spiral galaxies – nearby cities of stars like our own Milky Way. They can't be seen with the unaided eye, but a sweep along the lion's tummy with a small telescope will reveal them.

### PLANETS ON VIEW

The 'Goddess of Love' conquers the 'King of the Gods' this month. **Venus** is in the ascendant in the evening sky to the west, setting around 0.30 am all month. At magnitude −4.3, the glorious Evening Star passes through the fringes of

▼ The sky at 11 pm in mid-April, with Moon positions at three-day intervals either side of Full Moon. The star positions are also correct for midnight at the beginning of

*April, and 10 pm at the end of the month. The planets move slightly relative to the stars during the month.*

the Pleiades on 2 and 3 April (see Special Events). Through a small telescope, you can see its shape change from half-illuminated to a crescent as Venus approaches Earth.

Meanwhile, giant planet **Jupiter** – which has been a feature of the skies since last August – slips down into the dusk twilight. Shining at magnitude −1.9 in Aries, Jupiter is setting at 10.30 pm at the beginning of April, but it is lost in the Sun's glare by the end of the month.

**Mars** is visible all night in Leo: to its right lies the constellation's principal star, Regulus. As the faster-moving Earth pulls away during April, the Red Planet fades from magnitude −0.7 to 0.0.

But the honours this month belong to **Saturn** (see April's Object). The ring-world is at opposition on 15 April and visible all night in Virgo. At magnitude +0.5, it's a little brighter than nearby Spica, the brightest star in the constellation.

**Mercury** is technically a morning star this month, at greatest western elongation on 18 April, but it's lost in the bright dawn glow – as are **Uranus** and **Neptune**.

### MOON

The Moon lies below Mars on 3 April, with Regulus to Mars' right. On the night of 6/7 April, you'll find Saturn and Spica to the left of the Full Moon. The waning Moon lies above Antares on the morning of 10 April. The thinnest of crescent Moons lies above Jupiter just after sunset on 22 April. On 24 April, the Moon is near Venus in the evening sky.

WEST

THE MILKY WAY

GEMINI

Procyon

CANIS MINOR

27 Apr

CANCER

Castor
Pollux

Regulus

HYDRA

Algieba

LEO

Mars

3 Apr

URSA MAJOR

Denebola

Zenith

CANES VENATICI

VIRGO

CORVUS

The Plough

Arcturus

6 Apr

Spica

BOÖTES

CORONA BOREALIS

Saturn

Ecliptic

SERPENS

LIBRA

HERCULES

SOUTH

SE

OPHIUCHUS

EAST

Venus

Mars

Saturn

Moon

April's Object
Saturn

April's Picture
Virgo

Radiant of
Lyrids

| MOON | | |
|------|------|-------|
| Date | Time | Phase |
| 6 | 8.19 pm | Full Moon |
| 13 | 11.50 am | Last Quarter |
| 21 | 8.18 am | New Moon |
| 29 | 10.58 am | First Quarter |

19

The Moon lies to the lower right of bright-red Mars on 30 April, with Regulus in between.

### SPECIAL EVENTS

On **2** and **3 April**, Venus passes through the fringes of the Pleiades (Seven Sisters) star cluster – the jewel in an already exquisite crown, as seen in binoculars or a small telescope.

**21/22 April**: It's the maximum of the **Lyrid** meteor shower, which – by perspective – appears to emanate from the constellation of Lyra. The shower consists of particles from Comet Thatcher. With the Moon out of the way, this should be an excellent Lyrids year.

### APRIL'S OBJECT

The slowly moving ringworld **Saturn** is currently livening up the sprawling constellation Virgo (the Virgin). It's famed for its huge engirdling appendages: the rings would stretch nearly all the way from the Earth to the Moon. The ringed planet is a glorious sight through a small telescope, like an exquisite model hanging in space.

▼ *From Tenerife in the Canary Islands, Robin Scagell captured this image of Virgo using a 28 mm f/2.8 lens. The exposure time was 2 minutes on Ektachrome P1600 film.*

And the rings are just the beginnings of Saturn's larger family. It has at least 62 moons, including Titan – which is also visible through a small telescope. The international Cassini-Huygens mission has discovered lakes of liquid methane and ethane on Titan, and possibly active volcanoes. And the latest exciting news is that Cassini has imaged plumes of salty water spewing from its icy moon Enceladus. These discoveries raise the intriguing possibility of life on Saturn's moons.

Saturn itself is second only to Jupiter in size. But it's so low in density that were you to plop it in an ocean, it would float. Like Jupiter, Saturn has a ferocious spin rate – 10 hours and 32 minutes – and its winds roar at speeds of up to 1800 km/h.

Saturn's atmosphere is much blander than that of its larger cousin. But it's wracked with lightning-bolts 1000 times more

**⊙ Viewing tip**
Don't think that you need a telescope to bring the heavens closer. Binoculars are excellent – and you can fling them into the back of the car at the last minute. But when you buy binoculars, make sure that you get those with the biggest lenses, coupled with a modest magnification. Binoculars are described, for instance, as being '7×50' – meaning that the magnification is seven times, and that the diameter of the lenses is 50 mm across. These are ideal for astronomy – they have good light grasp, and the low magnification means that they don't exaggerate the wobbles of your arms too much. It's always best to rest your binoculars on a wall or a fence to steady the image. Some amateurs are the lucky owners of huge binoculars – say, 20×70 – with which you can see the rings of Saturn (being so large, these need a special mounting). But above all, never buy binoculars with small lenses that promise huge magnifications – they're a total waste of money.

powerful than those on Earth. And sometimes a giant storm bursts upwards to appear as a 'white spot': the most recent was in 2010.

## APRIL'S PICTURE

The constellation of **Virgo** is the epitome of spring. This Y-shaped pattern of stars cradles a plethora of galaxies in its bowl – a lovely sight through a small telescope (see May's Object). Brilliant **Spica** (bottom of image) is the constellation's principal star. It is very luminous – more than 12,000 times brighter than the Sun – and it spins very rapidly. Spica will almost certainly self-destruct as a supernova. This month, Virgo's Y-shape is distorted by an interloper: the planet Saturn.

## APRIL'S TOPIC
### Dark matter

We think of the Universe as a glorious, luminous entity: alight with shining stars, planets and galaxies. But nothing could be further from the truth. In recent years, astronomers have discovered that around 90% of our cosmos is invisible – taking the form of mysterious 'dark matter'.

Suspicions were aroused when researchers measured how quickly galaxies rotated. Their outer regions were spinning much faster than expected. The culprit had to be something exerting a strong gravitational force on the galaxies' peripheries. But what? There was nothing to be seen. However, something had to be there. Hence the search for dark matter.

Without knowing the nature of dark matter, it's hard to know how to find it – it's rather like looking for a black cat in a coal cellar! But physicists are hot on its trail. They are using a working potash mine in Yorkshire to winkle out these bizarre particles. Boulby Mine is over a kilometre below the ground, and shielded from radiation that could confuse the researchers' detectors.

At the moment, the best bet on dark matter is that it is made up of WIMPs – a wonderful acronym for 'weakly-interacting massive particles'. In theory, these particles were created in the Big Bang, and should still be around today. But scientists honestly don't know. So – watch this space!

Summer is on the way! The winter constellations of Orion and Taurus have been banished below the horizon, and the pretty star-patterns of our balmy months are taking over the heavens. A sure sign that warmer days are here is the appearance of **Arcturus** – a distinctly orange-coloured star that lords it over a huge area of sky devoid of other bright stars. This red giant is the brightest star in the constellation of **Boötes** (the Herdsman), who shepherds the two bears through the heavens.

### MAY'S CONSTELLATION

**Ursa Major**, the Great Bear, is one of everyone's favourite star-patterns. Its seven brightest stars are usually called '**the Plough**'. But unlike the brilliant stars of Orion, which make up the shape of a convincing superhero, those of the Plough are fainter. And most people today have probably never seen an old-fashioned, horse-drawn plough, from which the constellation takes its name. In fact, some children call it 'the saucepan', while in America it's known as 'the Big Dipper'.

But the Plough is the first constellation that most people get to know. There are two reasons. First, it's always on view in the northern hemisphere. And second, the two end stars of the 'bowl' of the Plough point directly towards the Pole Star, **Polaris**.

Though it seems so familiar, Ursa Major is unusual in a couple of ways. First, it contains a double star that you can actually split with the naked eye. **Mizar**, the star in the middle of the bear's tail (or the handle of the saucepan) has a fainter companion, **Alcor**.

And – unlike most constellations – most of the stars of the Plough lie at the same distance and were born together. Leaving aside the two end stars, **Dubhe** and **Alkaid**, the others are all moving in the same direction (along with brilliant Sirius, which is also a member of the group). Over

▼ The sky at 11 pm in mid-May, with Moon positions at three-day intervals either side of Full Moon. The star positions are also correct for midnight at the beginning of

*May, and 10 pm at the end of the month. The planets move slightly relative to the stars during the month.*

thousands of years, the shape of the Plough will gradually change, as Dubhe and Alkaid go off on their own paths.

## PLANETS ON VIEW

Regrettably, brilliant **Venus** – which has illuminated our evening skies since the beginning of the year – is no longer with us by month's end. At the start of May, the Evening Star sets at 0.30 am, over four hours after the Sun. But it takes a nosedive into the twilight glow, fading from magnitude −4.4 to −3.9, and disappears by the close of the month. Through a small telescope, you'll see the crescent Venus rapidly slimming as the planet approaches Earth. The star near Venus is El Nath, the upper horn of Taurus.

**Mars**, in Leo, is setting around 4.00 am at the beginning of the month, and 2.00 am at the end of May. As Earth pulls away from the Red Planet, its brightness drops from magnitude 0.0 to +0.5.

In the neighbouring constellation Virgo, **Saturn** shines all night long at a very similar magnitude (+0.6). The yellow planet makes a striking contrast with the nearby bright blue-white star Spica.

**Neptune** is now re-emerging in the morning sky, rising around 2.30 am. At magnitude +7.9, it lies in Aquarius.

**Mercury**, **Jupiter** and **Uranus** are all too close to the Sun to be visible this month.

## MOON

On the night of 4/5 May, the Moon is below Saturn, with Spica lying between

| | Venus |
| | Mars |
| | Saturn |
| | Moon |

[O] May's Object
Virgo Cluster

| MOON | | |
|---|---|---|
| **Date** | **Time** | **Phase** |
| 6 | 4.35 am | Full Moon |
| 12 | 10.47 pm | Last Quarter |
| 21 | 0.47 am | New Moon |
| 28 | 9.16 pm | First Quarter |

WEST

CANCER
27 May
The Sickle
Regulus
Mars
HYDRA
URSA MAJOR
LEO
CANES VENATICI
M87
Virgo Cluster
3 May
CORVUS
BOÖTES
The Plough
Mizar/Alcor
Zenith
Alkaid
VIRGO
Saturn
Spica
HYDRA
CENTAURUS
SOUTH
Arcturus
Ecliptic
CORONA BOREALIS
SERPENS
LIBRA
6 May
HERCULES
OPHIUCHUS
SCORPIUS
Antares
AQUILA
THE MILKY WAY
SE
Altair
SERPENS

EAST

them. In the early hours of 8 May, the star to the right of the Moon is Antares. You'll find the crescent Moon making a lovely pairing with Venus on 22 May. On 28 May, Mars lies to the upper left of the First Quarter Moon, and Regulus to its upper right; the following night (29 May), the Moon is to the left of Mars. And on 31 May, the Moon lies below Saturn and Spica.

### SPECIAL EVENTS

The maximum of the Eta Aquarid meteor shower falls on **4/5 May**, when tiny pieces of Halley's Comet burn up in Earth's atmosphere. Unfortunately, strong moonlight will drown out all but the brightest shooting stars this year.

There's a solar eclipse on **20/21 May**, but it's not visible from the UK. This annular eclipse – where the Moon appears too small to cover the Sun's face entirely – can be seen in the North Pacific, from China and Japan to California and New Mexico. A partial eclipse is visible from Siberia and north-western North America.

### MAY'S OBJECT

If you have a small telescope, sweep the 'bowl' formed by Virgo's 'Y' shape, and you'll detect dozens of fuzzy blobs. These are just a handful of the thousands of galaxies making up the **Virgo Cluster**: our closest giant cluster of galaxies, lying at a distance of 55 million light years.

Galaxies are gregarious. Thanks to gravity, they like living in groups. Our Milky Way, and the neighbouring giant spiral, the Andromeda Galaxy, live in a small cluster of about 30 modest galaxies called the Local Group.

But the Virgo Cluster is in a different league: it's like a vast galactic swarm of bees. What's more, its enormous gravity

### ◉ Viewing tip

When you first go out to observe, you may be disappointed at how few stars you can see in the sky. But wait for around 20 minutes, and you'll be amazed at how your night vision improves. One reason for this 'dark adaption' is that the pupil of your eye gets larger to make the best of the darkness. More importantly, in dark conditions the retina of your eye builds up much bigger reserves of rhodopsin, the chemical that responds to light.

holds sway over the smaller groups around – including our Local Group – to make a cluster of clusters of galaxies, the Virgo Supercluster.

The 2000 galaxies in the Virgo Cluster are also mega. Many of them are spirals like our Milky Way – including the famous 'Sombrero Hat', which looks just like its namesake – but some are even more spectacular. The heavyweight galaxy of the cluster is **M87**, a giant elliptical galaxy emitting a jet of gas over 4000 light years long and travelling at one-tenth the speed of light.

## MAY'S PICTURE

As summer approaches, look to the north to spot elusive **noctilucent clouds**. These ghostly blue wraiths of light are quite unlike any cloud in the sky. They form much higher than normal clouds, at altitudes above 80 kilometres – and they glow with an almost electric light. These mysterious clouds are lit from below by the Sun, and are thought to consist of particles of meteoric dust coated with ice.

## MAY'S TOPIC
### Star colours

Spring is well and truly here, with Arcturus gracing our night skies again. The fourth-brightest star in the sky, it follows the two bears around the heavens. In legend, Arcturus was 'the Bearkeeper' – responsible in particular for looking after Arcas, the Little Bear.

Look at the colour of Arcturus. It's orange-red: a sure sign that 'the Bearkeeper' is a cool star. Its surface temperature is just 4000°C, as compared to 5500°C for our yellow Sun.

Star colours are a good guide to their temperatures. The hottest stars are blue-white. White stars come next; then yellow, orange, and red.

Arcturus is a red giant: a distended star close to the end of its life. Its atmosphere has expanded, and cooled. But it's no match for Antares in Scorpius, which is just rising in the east. This bloated, baleful red star got its name from 'Anti Ares' – the rival of Mars.

Antares is 700 times the size of our Sun. If placed in the Solar System, it would stretch all the way to the asteroid belt. Now – in its death throes – the star's temperature has dropped to a mere 3200°C.

Contrast this with Spica, the bright, conspicuously blue-white star at the heart of Virgo. This is a star in the prime of life. Spica boasts a surface temperature of 22,000°C, and is more than 12,000 times brighter than the Sun.

◄ *From Northamptonshire, Jamie Cooper captured this image of noctilucent clouds. He used a Canon 5D camera set at ISO 200, with a 24 mm lens, and an exposure of 8 seconds. The picture was taken on 17 June 2009 at 11.42 pm.*

This month isn't the best time of the year to go stargazing! The Sun reaches its highest position over the northern hemisphere in June, so we get the longest days and shortest nights. The Summer Solstice this year takes place on 21 June, and the height of summer will be celebrated at festivals around the northern hemisphere on this day – notably at Stonehenge.

This seasonal ritual traces its roots back through millennia, and has led to the construction of massive stone monuments aligned on the rising Sun at midsummer. Our ancestors clearly had formidable astronomical knowledge.

Light nights apart, take advantage of the soft, warm weather to acquaint yourself with the lovely summer constellations of **Hercules**, **Scorpius**, **Lyra**, **Cygnus** and **Aquila**.

## JUNE'S CONSTELLATION

For one of antiquity's super-heroes, the celestial version of **Hercules** looks like a wimp. While Orion is all strutting masculinity, Hercules is but a poor reflection – and upside-down to boot!

The two constellations are similar in shape – you can see the outline of a man up there – but the stars are faint and un-distinguished. It's a shame because Hercules was one of the ancient Greeks' main legends, famous for his 12 labours of heroism.

Dig a little deeper, however, and you'll find a fascin-ating constellation. Outside the rectangular main 'body' of the hero, and to the south, lies **Rasalgethi** – Hercules' head. At 600 times the Sun's girth, this is one of the biggest stars known. This distended object, close to the end of its life, flops and billows in its death throes. As a result, it varies in brightness, changing from third to fourth magnitude over a period of about 90 days.

Hercules boasts one of the most spectacular sights in the northern night sky. Go back to the 'rectangle' and look about a quarter of the way down from the top right-hand star

▼ *The sky at 11 pm in mid-June, with Moon positions at three-day intervals either side of Full Moon. The star positions are also correct for midnight at the beginning of*

EAST

*June, and 10 pm at the end of the month. The planets move slightly relative to the stars during the month.*

(**eta Herculis** – a sun-like star), and you'll see a fuzzy patch. In a small telescope, **M13** – a globular cluster made of almost a million stars – looks like a swarm of bees

## PLANETS ON VIEW

During June, **Mars** moves from Leo to Virgo, fading from magnitude +0.5 to +0.8, as its setting time advances from 2.00 am to 0.20 am. On the nights of 27 and 28 June, Mars is only one-third of a degree from Zavijah (magnitude +3.5) which marks the end of the lower arm of Virgo's 'Y' shape.

**Saturn** lies on the other side of Virgo, above the constellation's principal star, Spica. At magnitude +0.8, the ringworld is setting at 3.20 am at the beginning of June, and at 1.20 am by the end of the month.

You may catch **Mercury** (magnitude 0.0) very low in the north-west after sunset during the second half of the month: it's best seen around 20 June when the elusive planet sets one-and-a-half hours after the Sun.

**Neptune**, at magnitude +7.9, rises about 0.30 am in Aquarius. It's followed by **Uranus** (magnitude +5.9), lying on the borders of Pisces and Cetus and rising around 1.30 am.

From mid-June onwards, there's quite a planetary buzz in the morning sky. After passing right in front of the Sun on 6 June (see Special Events), **Venus** reappears in the north-east around 15 June. From magnitude −4.0, the Morning Star brightens to −4.4 by month's end, when it's rising by 3.15 am.

| MOON | | |
|---|---|---|
| **Date** | **Time** | **Phase** |
| 4 | 12.11 pm | Full Moon |
| 11 | 11.41 am | Last Quarter |
| 19 | 4.02 pm | New Moon |
| 27 | 4.30 am | First Quarter |

June's Object
Delta Cephei

Mars
Saturn
Moon

To the upper right of Venus you'll find **Jupiter**. Lying in Taurus – just under the Pleiades – the giant planet shines at magnitude −1.9 and rises around 2.30 am.

## MOON

The Moon is near Antares on the night of 3/4 June. The dawn skies of 17 June see the thin crescent Moon next to Jupiter, with Venus rising to the lower left. Just before sunrise on 18 June, you may catch the slimmest of crescent Moons to the left of Venus. In the evening sky, there's another narrow crescent Moon lying below Mercury on 21 June. You'll find the Moon close to Regulus on 24 June; and near to Mars on 25 and 26 June. On 28 June, the Moon lies to the left of Saturn and Spica.

## SPECIAL EVENTS

On **4 June**, there's a partial eclipse of the Moon, visible from the Pacific Ocean and countries all around it – but not from Britain.

Venus crosses the Sun's face on **6 June**. From the UK, we'll catch only the last hour of the transit, after sunrise at 4.45 am. To see the whole event, you will need to be in Australia, China, Japan, Siberia or the western Pacific. **DO NOT LOOK DIRECTLY AT THE SUN** – see this month's 'Viewing tip'.

**21 June**, 0.09 am: Summer Solstice. The Sun reaches its most northerly point in the sky, so 21 June is Midsummer's Day, with the longest period of daylight. Correspondingly, we have the shortest nights.

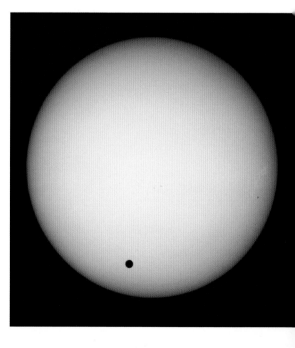

▼ Jamie Cooper took this image of the transit of Venus on 8 June 2004. He used a 90 mm Maksutov-Cassegrain telescope, with a Canon 300D camera working at ISO 200.

## JUNE'S OBJECT

At first glance, the star **Delta Cephei** – in the constellation representing King **Cepheus** – doesn't seem to merit any special attention. It's a yellowish star of magnitude +4, easily visible to the naked eye, but not prominent. A telescope reveals a companion star – but this star holds the key to the size of the Universe.

Check the brightness of this star carefully over days and weeks, and you'll see that its brightness changes regularly, from +3.6 (brightest) to +4.3 (faintest), every 5 days 9 hours. It's a result of the star literally swelling and shrinking in size, from 32 to 35 times the Sun's diameter.

Astronomers have found that stars like this – Cepheid variables – show a

This is the month for maximum Sun-viewing, and a chance to catch the end of the transit of Venus on 6 June – but be careful. NEVER use a telescope or binoculars to look at the Sun directly: it could blind you permanently. Fogged film is no safer, because it allows the Sun's infra-red (heat) rays to get through. Eclipse goggles are safe (unless they're scratched). The simplest way to observe the Sun is to project its image through binoculars or a telescope on to a white piece of card. There's more advice on safe solar observation in the Equipment Review (pages 61–64).

link between their period of variation and their intrinsic luminosity. By observing the star's period and brightness as it appears in the sky, astronomers can work out a Cepheid's distance. With the Hubble Space Telescope, astronomers have now measured Cepheids in the Virgo Cluster of galaxies, which lies 55 million light years away.

## JUNE'S PICTURE

Neighbour–world **Venus** drifts across the face of the Sun in this image. The transit on 6 June this year is a rare event, and well worth watching – and capturing on camera! Timing and observing transits of Venus used to be a valuable means to work out the scale of our Solar System: many countries instigated expeditions in the past, leaving impressive memorials at the transit sites.

## JUNE'S TOPIC
### A star's life

We think of the stars as being constant and unchanging, but a long, leisurely look at the summer sky proves anything but. Sweep Sagittarius with binoculars, and you'll find it studded with nebulae – gas clouds which are the nurseries of new stars. These fledgling stars grow up to make hot young stars like Vega, shining as a result of nuclear reactions in their searingly-hot cores. As stars age – and their hydrogen fuel starts to run out – they develop the problems of middle age. Look no further than orange Arcturus and baleful red Antares (in Scorpius) for stars that have swollen up and cooled down near the end of their lives. Stars like these will eventually puff off their distended atmospheres into space, leaving a brief-lived 'planetary nebula' (like the Dumbbell – see August's Object), surrounding the now-defunct core. The nebula will soon disperse, leaving the cooling core – a white dwarf – alone in space, destined to become a cold, black cinder.

More massive stars, like Orion's Betelgeuse, undergo more complex nuclear reactions, as a result of their mighty gravity. They can build up elements in their cores all the way up to iron. But when they try to fuse iron, all hell breaks loose. Instead of creating energy, the reaction takes *in* energy. As a result, the core collapses in an inferno that makes the star explode as a supernova. The dead core may collapse totally, to become a black hole.

This July is a month for stars, rather than planets. Gaze at the **Summer Triangle** as it soars overhead. **Vega, Deneb** and **Altair** are each the brightest star in their own constellation: Vega in **Lyra**, Deneb in **Cygnus**, and Altair in **Aquila**. And this is the time to catch the far-southern constellations of **Sagittarius** and **Scorpius** – embedded in the glorious heart of the Milky Way.

▼ The sky at 11 pm in mid-July, with Moon positions at three-day intervals either side of Full Moon. The star positions are also correct for midnight at the beginning of

## JULY'S CONSTELLATION

Down in the deep south of the sky this month lies a baleful red star. This is **Antares** – 'the rival of Mars' – and in its ruddiness it even surpasses the famed Red Planet. To ancient astronomers, Antares marked the heart of **Scorpius**, the celestial scorpion.

According to Greek myth, this summer constellation is intimately linked with the winter star-pattern Orion, who was killed by a mighty scorpion. The gods immortalized these two opponents as star-patterns, set at opposite ends of the sky so that Orion sets as Scorpius rises.

Scorpius is one of the few constellations that look like their name-sakes. To the top right of Antares, a line of stars marks the scorpion's fore-limbs. Originally, the stars we now call **Libra** (the Scales) were its claws. Below Antares, the scorpion's body stretches down into a fine curved tail (below the horizon on the chart), and deadly sting.

Scorpius is a treasure-trove of astronomical goodies. Several lovely double stars include Antares: its faint companion looks greenish in contrast to Antares' strong red hue. Binoculars reveal the fuzzy patch of **M4**, a globular cluster made of tens of thousands of stars, some 7200 light years away.

The 'sting' contains two fine star clusters – **M6** and **M7** – so near to us that we can see them with the naked eye: a telescope reveals their stars clearly.

*July, and 10 pm at the end of the month. The planets move slightly relative to the stars during the month.*

## PLANETS ON VIEW

**Mercury** skulks very low in the north-west after sunset for the first couple of days of July: it reaches greatest eastern elongation on 1 July, but is too faint to be easily seen, at magnitude +0.7.

**Mars** spends the month in Virgo, heading towards Saturn and Spica. It's setting around 0.20 am at the beginning of July, and 10.50 pm at the end of the month. The Red Planet is fading, from magnitude +0.9 to +1.1 as the Earth pulls away from slower-moving Mars.

Also in Virgo, you'll find **Saturn** (magnitude +0.8) near to the star Spica, which is just a little fainter, at magnitude +1.0. The ringworld sets at 1.20 am at the start of the month, and at 11.20 pm by the end of July.

A small telescope reveals **Neptune** in Aquarius, at magnitude +7.8, rising about 10.30 pm.

Use binoculars to hunt out **Uranus** (magnitude +5.8), rising around 11.30 pm on the borders of Pisces and Cetus.

Jupiter and Venus still make a fine pair in the pre-dawn skies. **Jupiter** lies to the upper right: at magnitude −1.9 it lies in Taurus, rising at 2.30 am at the beginning of July, and by 1.00 am at the end of the month. It is near the star omega-2 Tauri on the mornings of 10 and 11 July (see Special Events). Even more spectacularly, on the morning of 15 July, Jupiter is occulted by the Moon (see Special Events).

The Morning Star, **Venus**, starts the month in the Hyades star cluster, though the bright dawn sky will make

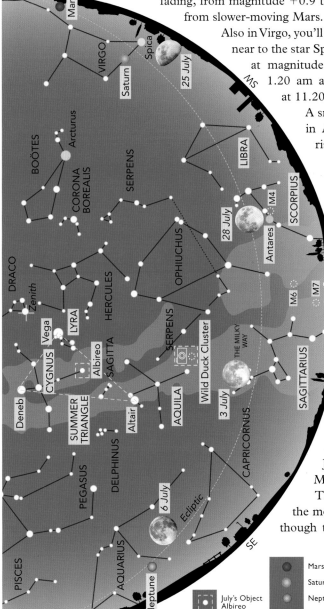

| Mars |
| Saturn |
| Neptune |
| July's Object Albireo |
| July's Picture Wild Duck Cluster |
| Moon |

| MOON | | |
|---|---|---|
| Date | Time | Phase |
| 3 | 7.52 pm | Full Moon |
| 11 | 2.48 am | Last Quarter |
| 19 | 5.24 am | New Moon |
| 26 | 9.56 am | First Quarter |

it difficult to discern the surrounding stars. It's close to Aldebaran on the morning of 9 July.

## MOON

On 1 July, the almost-Full Moon lies near Antares. In the early hours of 15 July, the crescent Moon lies so close to Jupiter that it occults the giant planet (see Special Events), with Venus picturesquely set below. Before dawn on 16 July, you'll see Venus and – higher in the sky – Jupiter to the right of the crescent Moon. On 24 July, the Moon lies below Mars; the following night (25 July) the Moon is near Spica, with Saturn above. The star below the Moon on 28 July is Antares.

## SPECIAL EVENTS

On **5 July**, the Earth is at aphelion, its furthest point from the Sun.

Jupiter lies very close to omega-2 Tauri (magnitude +4.9) on the mornings of **10** and **11 July**, and – through binoculars or a small telescope – it looks as though Jupiter's four bright moons have suddenly increased to five!

On the morning of **15 July**, Jupiter is occulted by the Moon, as seen from the southernmost parts of the UK (or, even better, from Europe). This rare event begins at 2.55 am and ends at 3.10 am.

And **sometime this month**, the asteroid-probe DAWN should leave Vesta after a year in orbit, and head for its bigger sibling Ceres.

## JULY'S OBJECT

The constellation Cygnus represents a soaring swan, her wings outspread as she flies down the Milky Way. The lowest star in Cygnus, marking the swan's head, is **Albireo**. The name looks Arabic, but it actually has no meaning and is merely the result of errors in translation, from Greek to Arabic to Latin.

Binoculars reveal that Albireo is actually two stars in one. Use a telescope, and you'll be treated to one of the most glorious sky-sights – a dazzling yellow star teamed up with a blue companion.

The yellow star is a giant, near the end of its life. It's 80 times bigger than the Sun, and 1000 times brighter. The fainter blue companion is 'only' 95 times brighter than the Sun.

The spectacular colour contrast is due to the stars' different temperatures. The giant star is slightly cooler than our Sun, and shines with a yellowish glow. The smaller companion is far hotter: it is so incandescent that it shines not merely white-hot, but blue-white.

▶ *Michael Stecker in California took this single exposure of the Wild Duck Cluster through an Astrophysics 155 mm f/7 EDF refractor. He used Kodak Pro 400 negative film with an exposure time of 55 minutes.*

◉ **Viewing tip**

This is the month when you really need a good, unobstructed view to the southern horizon to make out the summer constellations of Scorpius and Sagittarius. They never rise high in temperate latitudes, so make the best of a southerly view – especially over the sea – if you're away on holiday. A good southern horizon is also best for views of the planets, because they rise highest when they're in the south.

## JULY'S PICTURE

The **Wild Duck Cluster** in Scutum contains 2900 stars, born 220 million years ago. A lovely sight through a small telescope, it was discovered in 1681 by Gottfried Kirsch. Its name derives from the triangular shape created by its brightest stars, resembling a formation of flying ducks.

## JULY'S TOPIC
### Centre of the Milky Way

The Milky Way stretches all the way around our sky, as a gently glowing band. In reality, it is a spiral shape of some 200–400 billion stars, with the Sun about halfway out. The centre of the Milky Way lies in the direction of the constellation Sagittarius. But our view of the galactic centre is obscured by great clouds of dark dust that block the view for even the most powerful telescopes.

Now, however, instruments observing at other wavelengths have lifted the veil on the Galaxy's heart. Infrared and radio telescopes can pick out stars and gas clouds at the galactic centre. These objects are speeding around so fast that they must be in the grip of something with fantastically strong gravity. In 2002, a team of astronomers at the European Southern Observatory, in Chile, discovered a star that's orbiting the Galaxy's centre at over 18 million km/h! In the meantime, radio astronomers have found that the Galaxy's exact heart is marked by a tiny source of radiation: Sagittarius A★.

Putting all these observations together, astronomers have concluded that the core of the Milky Way must contain a supermassive black hole: it's estimated that it weighs in at 4 million Suns. When a speeding star comes too close to this invisible monster, it's ripped apart. There's a final shriek from the star's gases – producing the observed radio waves – before they fall into the black hole, and disappear from our Universe.

The evening sky is enlightened by a dance of two planets – Mars and Saturn – with the star Spica, and a special light show on 12/13 August, when we are treated to a display from the **Perseid** meteor shower.

▼ *The sky at 11 pm in mid-August, with Moon positions at three-day intervals either side of Full Moon. The star positions are also correct for midnight*

### AUGUST'S CONSTELLATION

It has to be admitted that **Aquila** does vaguely resemble a flying eagle, albeit a rather faint one. It's an ancient constellation, named after the bird which was a companion to the god Jupiter – and even carried his thunderbolts for him! The constellation is dominated by **Altair**, a young blue-white star 17 light years away, which is 11 times brighter than our Sun. It has a very fast spin: the star hurtles around at 210 km/s, rotating in just 10.4 hours (as opposed to about 30 days for the Sun). As a result, it is oval in shape. Altair is a triple star, and its neighbour **beta Aquilae** (just below, left) is double. **Eta Aquilae** (below beta) is one of the brightest Cepheid variable stars – old stars which change their brightness by swelling and shrinking. The pulsations of eta Aquilae make it vary from magnitude +3.5 to +4.4 every seven days.

### PLANETS ON VIEW

**Saturn** is the brightest planet in the evening sky: at magnitude +1.0 it's a near twin to Spica, which lies below it in Virgo. The ringworld is setting at 11.15 pm at the start of August, but disappears by 9.30 pm at the end of the month.

Also in Virgo, and slightly fainter than Saturn – at magnitude +1.2 – **Mars** calls attention to itself with a spectacular dash across the sky. The Red Planet starts out to the right of Saturn and Spica, dashes between them (see Special Events) on 13/14 August, and ends the month well to the left, near the border with Libra. Mars sets at 10.45 pm at the beginning of the month, and 9.25 pm at the end of August.

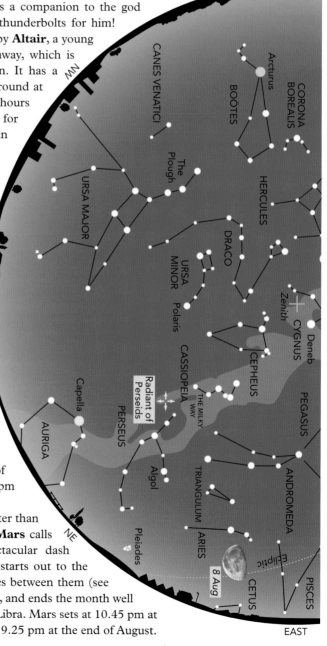

*at the beginning of August, and 10 pm at the end of the month. The planets move slightly relative to the stars during the month.*

**Neptune** (magnitude +7.8) lies in Aquarius and rises at about 8.30 pm. On 24 August, the most distant planet is at opposition and lies closest to Earth – a 'mere' 4.3 billion kilometres!

You'll need to wait until 9.40 pm for its nearer twin, **Uranus**, to rise: at magnitude +5.8, it's sitting on the fence between Pisces and Cetus.

**Jupiter** is beginning to pull its weight this month, shining at magnitude −2.1 in Taurus. The giant planet rises just before 1 am at the start of August, and at 11.10 pm at the close of the month. Jupiter lies near the Hyades star cluster, with the Pleiades to the upper right.

Dazzling **Venus** is now rising almost four hours before the Sun. At magnitude −4.2, the Morning Star outshines everything in the night sky – bar the Moon – and is visible almost until the Sun rises. It's at greatest elongation on 15 August.

Just a day later (16 August) **Mercury** is also at elongation, as a much less lustrous morning star at magnitude +0.1. That morning, you'll find Mercury just to the upper left of the crescent Moon: it's visible for a few mornings before and after elongation.

## MOON

The Moon lies near Jupiter on the night of 11/12 August, and near Venus in the mornings of 13 and 14 August. In the dawn sky of 16 August, the very thin crescent Moon hangs to the lower

WEST

EAST

| Key | | | |
|---|---|---|---|
| August's Object Dumbbell Nebula | | | Uranus |
| August's Picture Delphinus | | | Neptune |
| Radiant of Perseids | | | Moon |

| MOON | | |
|---|---|---|
| Date | Time | Phase |
| 2 | 4.27 am | Full Moon |
| 9 | 7.55 pm | Last Quarter |
| 17 | 4.55 pm | New Moon |
| 24 | 2.53 pm | First Quarter |
| 31 | 2.58 pm | Full Moon |

right of Mercury. The Moon forms a striking group with Mars, Saturn and Spica very low in the western evening sky on 21 and 22 August. On 24 August, the First Quarter Moon is near Antares.

### SPECIAL EVENTS

Around 6 **August**, NASA's Curiosity rover should land on Mars. Curiosity will drill into the Red Planet's rocks to check out its geology and past climatic history – but it's not directly looking for Martian life.

The maximum of the annual **Perseid** meteor shower falls on **12/13 August**. It's among the year's most prolific displays of shooting stars, but marred this year by the Moon rising at 0.30 am.

On the evenings of **13** and **14 August**, you'll find Spica, Mars and Saturn in line. It's a great opportunity to compare colours in the heavens: the blue-white star, the yellow ringworld and – of course – the Red Planet. Binoculars will make the contrast more spectacular.

### AUGUST'S OBJECT

The tiny, faint constellation of Vulpecula (the Little Fox) contains one of the most beautiful sights in the sky – the **Dumbbell Nebula**. At magnitude +7.5, it is just visible through binoculars, and a real treat when seen through a telescope. Although an object of beauty, the Dumbbell is a denizen of doom. This 'planetary nebula' is the remains of a star that has died. The term was first coined by planet-discoverer William Herschel, who noted the resemblance of these circular nebulae to planets; it was his son John who nicknamed the Dumbbell, because 'it resembled a double-headed shot'.

The Dumbbell lies roughly 1360 light years away (distances to planetary nebulae are notoriously difficult to measure), and is an estimated 2.5 light years across. It was created when an ageing star ran out of hydrogen fuel in its core, and puffed off its enveloping atmosphere into space. From the expansion rate of the nebula, astronomers estimate that the fatal act took place some 10,000 years ago.

Nevertheless, a corpse still lingers at the heart of the nebula. In its centre is a tiny white dwarf star: the collapsed core of the former star. It has no source of energy – all it can do is leak away its heat into space. Although it has a surface temperature of over 80,000°C at the moment, it will eventually end up as a cold, black cinder.

## AUGUST'S PICTURE

Small but perfectly formed, the constellation of **Delphinus** (the Dolphin) rides high in our summer skies. This beautiful group of stars looks exactly like the plunging marine mammal that the ancient Greeks associated with saving sailors adrift on the high seas. The two brightest stars are called, respectively, Svalocin and Rotanev. Hardly traditional names: it turns out that, in 1814, the assistant director of the Palermo Observatory in Italy – Nicolaus Venator – named them after the latinized version of his name, spelt backwards!

## AUGUST'S TOPIC
### Perseid meteor shower

So many people report to us that they see loads of shooting stars on their summer holidays – and are amazed when we observe: 'So you go on holiday in August?' But there's no great mystery here. Between 8 and 17 August, Earth's orbit intersects a stream of debris from Comet Swift-Tuttle, which smashes into our atmosphere at speeds of 210,000 km/h and burns up. It forms the Perseids – the most reliable meteor shower of the year. Because of perspective, the meteors all appear to diverge from the same part of the sky – the *radiant* – which lies in the constellation Perseus. But there's no danger of being struck by a meteor. These tiny particles of dust (less than a centimetre across) burn up around 60 kilometres above the Earth's surface. Look upon the shower as a celestial fireworks display – with the added bonus that August is much warmer than Bonfire Night!

The autumn rains will have returned again – and we have wet star-patterns to match! **Aquarius** (the Water Carrier) is part of a group of aqueous star-patterns that include **Cetus** (the Sea Monster), **Capricornus** (the Sea Goat), **Pisces** (the Fishes), **Piscis Austrinus** (the Southern Fish) and **Delphinus** (the Dolphin). There's speculation that the ancient Babylonians associated this region with water because the Sun passed through this zone of the heavens during their rainy season, from February to March.

## SEPTEMBER'S CONSTELLATION

As we noted in the introduction, **Capricornus** is one of a group of wet and watery constellations that swim in the celestial sea below **Pegasus** (the Winged Horse). But Capricornus had a special significance for ancient peoples. Over 2500 years ago, the Sun nestled amongst its stars at the time of the Winter Solstice. It showed to them that the year was about to turn around: the hours of darkness were at an end, and life-giving spring was on the way. So this obscure triangle of faint stars may have been one of humanity's first constellations.

**Algedi** is the most interesting star in the constellation, lying at top right. Even with the unaided eye, you can see that the star is double. The pair are faint – magnitudes +3.6 and +4.6 respectively – and they aren't related. But each star is genuinely double, although you'll need a telescope to check this out.

By coincidence, the next-door star **Dabih** is also a double. The main member of this duo is a yellow star of magnitude +3.1; binoculars or a small telescope will reveal a blue companion at magnitude +6.

A telescope is also essential for the next beast in Capricornus – the globular cluster **M30**. The seventh-magnitude object, about 26,000 light years away, is just to the

▼ *The sky at 11 pm in mid-September, with Moon positions at three-day intervals either side of Full Moon. The star positions are also correct for midnight at*

WEST

OPHIUCHUS
SERPENS
CORONA BOREALIS
Arcturus
NW
CANES VENATICI
BOÖTES
HERCULES
Vega
LYRA
Deneb
The Plough
DRACO
CYGNUS
CEPHEUS
Zenith
URSA MAJOR
URSA MINOR
Polaris
CASSIOPEIA
NORTH
ANDROMEDA
TRIANGULUM
Capella
PERSEUS
Algol
AURIGA
THE MILKY WAY
Pleiades
6 Sept
Jupiter
Aldebaran
Ecliptic
TAURUS
NE

EAST

*the beginning of September, and 10 pm at the end of the month. The planets move slightly relative to the stars during the month.*

lower left of the constellation. This rather ragged ball of thousands of stars was probably among the first objects to form in our Galaxy. And it's very pretty – so, if you're into astrophotography, whether electronic or conventional – point and shoot!

## PLANETS ON VIEW

**Saturn** bows out this month; you may just catch the ringworld early in September, shining at magnitude +0.9 low in the west after sunset, and setting at 9.20 pm. But Saturn has sunk into the twilight glow by the end of September.

To the left of Saturn, rather fainter **Mars** (magnitude +1.2) is also moving towards the Sun – but at a slower rate. Assiduous fans of the Red Planet may be able to catch it in the dusk skies through to the close of the month. Like Saturn, it sets at 9.20 pm at the start of September, moving to 8.10 pm at month's end.

Distant **Neptune** still has its haunts in Aquarius. At magnitude +7.8, it sets at 4.30 am. And this month, on 29 September, it's opposition time for the penultimate planet **Uranus** (see September's Object): the planet is above the horizon all night, at magnitude +5.7 on the borders of Cetus and Pisces. On 23 September, Uranus passes only 1 arcminute (one-thirtieth the Moon's diameter) from a star of equal brightness, 44 Piscium. Brilliant **Jupiter** (magnitude −2.3) rises at 11 pm at the beginning of the month, and 9.20 pm by the end of September. You'll find the giant planet in Taurus, to the left of Aldebaran and the Hyades.

WEST

SERPENS · OPHIUCHUS · SERPENS · SAGITTARIUS · THE MILKY WAY · AQUILA · SAGITTA · Altair · DELPHINUS · Dabih · Algedi · CAPRICORNUS · 24 Sept · M30 · PISCIS AUSTRINUS · GRUS · SOUTH

HERCULES · LYRA · Vega · CYGNUS · Deneb · Zenith · PEGASUS · The Moon · Neptune

CEPHEUS · ANDROMEDA · Square of Pegasus · 27 Sept · AQUARIUS · Fomalhaut

TRIANGULUM · ARIES · PISCES · 30 Sept · Uranus · Ecliptic · CETUS · Mira

TAURUS · ERIDANUS · SE

EAST

| | | | MOON | | |
|---|---|---|---|---|---|
| Jupiter | | | | | |
| Uranus | | **Date** | **Time** | **Phase** | |
| Neptune | | 8 | 2.15 pm | Last Quarter | |
| Moon | | 16 | 3.11 am | New Moon | |
| | | 22 | 8.41 pm | First Quarter | |
| | | 30 | 4.19 am | Full Moon | |

September's Object
Uranus

September's Picture
The Moon

But Jupiter is put in the shade when glorious **Venus** rises, around 2.30 am – over four hours before the Sun. The Morning Star blazes at magnitude −4.0, moving from Gemini, through Cancer to Leo. On 13 September, Venus lies just below Praesepe (the Beehive star cluster)

**Mercury** is too close to the Sun to be seen this month.

## MOON

On the nights of 7/8 and 8/9 September, you'll find the Last Quarter Moon near Jupiter. The crescent Moon lies near Venus on the mornings of 12 and 13 September. In the evening sky, the Moon is close to Mars low in the south-west on 19 September.

## SPECIAL EVENTS

It's the Autumn Equinox at 3.49 pm on **22 September**. The Sun is over the Equator as it heads southwards in the sky, and day and night are equal.

## SEPTEMBER'S OBJECT

If you have extremely dark skies and are very sharp-sighted, you stand a chance of spotting **Uranus**, the most distant planet visible to the unaided eye. At magnitude +5.7 in Pisces, it is closest to Earth this year on 29 September. Discovered by amateur astronomer William Herschel in 1781, Uranus was the first planet to be found since antiquity. Then, it doubled the size of our Solar System. Uranus is a gas giant like Jupiter, Saturn and Neptune. Four times the diameter of the Earth, it has an odd claim to fame: it orbits the Sun on its side, probably as a result of a collision in its infancy that knocked it off its perch. Like the other gas giants, it has an encircling system of rings, but these are nothing like the spectacular edifices that girdle Saturn: the 11 rings are thin and faint. It also has a large family of moons, numbering 27 at the

▲ *Damian Peach took this picture of the lunar crater Arzachel from Flackwell Heath in Buckinghamshire. He used a 355 mm C14 telescope with a Lumenera SKYnyx camera to capture a video sequence. After the exposure, the sharpest frames were stacked and sharpened.*

◉ **Viewing tip**

It's best to view your favourite objects when they're well clear of the horizon. When you look low down, you're seeing through a large thickness of the atmosphere, which is always shifting and turbulent. It's like trying to observe the outside world from the bottom of a swimming pool! This turbulence makes the stars appear to twinkle. Low-down planets also twinkle – although to a lesser extent because they subtend tiny discs, and aren't so affected.

last count. Many of us were disappointed when the Voyager 2 probe flew past Uranus in 1986 to reveal a bland, featureless world. But things are hotting up as the planet's seasons change – streaks and clouds are appearing in its atmosphere. And scientists from the European Space Agency are hoping to find out more if their Uranus Pathfinder probe becomes reality.

## SEPTEMBER'S PICTURE

The ever-present **Moon** is always an object of beauty and wonder. Even with the unaided eye, you can see the results of the colossal bombardment that took place 3800 million years ago – creating the 'face' of the 'man in the moon'. This glorious close-up of the lunar crater Arzachel shows the result of a smaller, more recent impact – with a fresh, even younger crater within its massive walls. Arzachel measures 96 kilometres in diameter.

## SEPTEMBER'S TOPIC
### Formation of the Solar System

A cloud of dust and rubble, drifting in space, started to agglomerate 4567 million years ago. Gravity was the driver, but the cloud may have been given a kick from the blast-wave of a nearby supernova. This was the start of our Solar System.

How can we be so exact about the date of its birth? Radioactive elements (which have measured decay times) in meteorites act as cosmic clocks. And rare elements in these lumps of cosmic debris testify to the push from an exploding star.

At the centre of the nebula, heat and gravity were fierce. Nuclear reactions kicked in, and our infant Sun was born – flooding the Solar System with energy, and driving away the gases. So the inner planets – like the Earth – were made of accumulations of rock and rubble. The outer planets, like Jupiter and Saturn, wrapped themselves up as gas giants in their cooler environment.

Today, the violence of our Solar System's birth is still in evidence. Asteroids and meteorites continue to bombard planets – teaching us that space is a dangerous place, and that cosmic timescales are very long.

The constellations of October can hardly be described as 'gripping'. The barren **Square of Pegasus** dominates the southern sky, with unfortunate **Andromeda** attached to his side. But there are two glorious galaxies on view: the **Andromeda Galaxy** (see October's Object), and its smaller cousin the **Triangulum Galaxy** (see October's Picture). When you gaze upon these cosmic beauties, you are looking back over 2 million years in time.

▼ The sky at 11 pm in mid-October, with Moon positions at three-day intervals either side of Full Moon. The star positions are also correct for midnight at

### OCTOBER'S CONSTELLATION

**Pisces** is typical of the autumn constellations – faint and straggly. It loops around the sky below and to the lower left of **Pegasus**. For completely unknown reasons, many ancient civilizations – from the Babylonians to the Egyptians and the early Christians – saw the stars as a pair of fishes.

In Greek mythology, the constellation depicted the goddess Aphrodite and her son Eros, converted into fishes. They were tied together by a cord on their scaly tails, in order to escape from the monster Typhon.

In today's skies, the cord is marked by **Al Rischa** (whose name means 'cord' in Arabic). In 1779, William Herschel discovered that it is a double star. The pair circle each other every 720 years, and currently appear very close together. Wait until 2060 to see the components well separated.

Pisces' main claim to fame is that it is the location of the Vernal Equinox – the point in the sky where the Sun crosses the celestial equator on its way from the southern to the northern hemisphere. That location used to be 'the first point of Aries', but as a result of Earth's wobbling on its axis (precession), the point has now shifted from the constellation of Aries into Pisces. Precession is also the reason why astrological Sun-signs are not lined up with their original constellations.

WEST

OPHIUCHUS
AQUILA
NW
CORONA BOREALIS
HERCULES
LYRA
THE MILKY WAY
CYGNUS
Vega
BOÖTES
DRACO
Deneb
Zenith
CASSIOPEIA
CANES VENATICI
The Plough
CEPHEUS
URSA MINOR
Polaris
NORTH
PERSEUS
URSA MAJOR
Capella
AURIGA
Jupiter
Castor
GEMINI
Aldebaran
Pollux
Radiant of Orionids
Betelgeuse
5 Oct
NE
Ecliptic
ORION

EAST

*the beginning of October, and 9 pm at the end of the month (after the end of BST). The planets move slightly relative to the stars during the month.*

You'll have to wait 24,000 years for the Sun to rise in your 'real' star-sign again!

## PLANETS ON VIEW

Two faint planets are all we have in the early evening sky. **Neptune** (magnitude +7.9) lies in Aquarius, setting around 2.30 am. And slightly brighter **Uranus**, at magnitude +5.7, inhabits another watery constellation, Pisces. It sets about 6.00 am.

**Jupiter** bursts on to the scene at 9.15 pm at the start of October, and by 6.15 pm at the end of the month. At magnitude −2.5, the giant planet dominates the constellation of Taurus.

Resplendent at magnitude −3.9, **Venus** rises about 3.30 am. The Morning Star starts the month close to Regulus: on the morning of 3 October, it skims just 10 arcminutes (one-third the Moon's diameter) from the star.

**Saturn** is lost in the Sun's glare this month. **Mars** and **Mercury** are too low in the evening twilight to be seen from Britain, even though the innermost planet is at elongation on 26 October.

## MOON

The Moon passes under Jupiter on 5 October. In the morning of 12 October, the crescent Moon lies to the right of Venus, with Regulus above; and the following morning (13 October) you'll find the thin crescent Moon directly below Venus. Mars is close to the crescent Moon low in the evening sky on 18 October.

### Star chart labels

WEST · SW · SOUTH · SE · EAST

SERPENS · THE MILKY WAY · AQUILA · Altair · CYGNUS · SAGITTA · Deneb · DELPHINUS · Enif · Andromeda Galaxy · PEGASUS · Square of Pegasus · 23 Oct · CAPRICORNUS · AQUARIUS · Neptune · 26 Oct · Ecliptic · PISCIS AUSTRINUS · Fomalhaut · CASSIOPEIA · Zenith · ANDROMEDA · Triangulum Galaxy · Uranus · PISCES · CETUS · PERSEUS · Algol · TRIANGULUM · ARIES · 29 Oct · Al Rischa · Mira · Pleiades · TAURUS · ERIDANUS · Jupiter · 5 Oct · Aldebaran · Betelgeuse · ORION · Rigel

### Key

October's Object — Andromeda Galaxy

October's Picture — Triangulum Galaxy

Radiant of Orionids

Jupiter · Uranus · Neptune · Moon

### MOON

| Date | Time | Phase |
|---|---|---|
| 8 | 8.33 am | Last Quarter |
| 15 | 1.02 pm | New Moon |
| 22 | 4.32 pm | First Quarter |
| 29 | 7.50 pm | Full Moon |

◄ Peter Shah captured this beautiful photo of the Triangulum Galaxy from Meifod in Wales. He used a 200 mm telescope, with a CCD camera to take separate images through red, green and blue filters, plus an unfiltered exposure. The total exposure was 160 minutes.

## SPECIAL EVENTS

Russia's Phobos-Grunt mission is due to enter orbit around Mars about **9 October**, and release the small Chinese orbiter Yinghuo-1. Phobos-Grunt itself is scheduled to land on Mars' moon Phobos in February 2013.

Debris from Halley's Comet smashes into Earth's atmosphere on **20/21 October**, causing the **Orionid** meteor shower. It's a good year for these annual shooting stars, after the Moon sets at 10 pm.

At 2 am on **28 October**, we see the end of British Summer Time for this year. Clocks go backwards by an hour.

## OCTOBER'S OBJECT

Take advantage of autumn's new-born darkness to pick out one of our neighbouring galaxies – M31 in **Andromeda**. M31 (the **Andromeda Galaxy**) is easily visible to the unaided eye from a dark location. It covers an area four times bigger than the Full Moon. Like our Milky Way, it is a beautiful spiral shape, but – alas – it's presented to us almost edge-on.

The Andromeda Galaxy lies around 2.5 million light years away, and it's similar in size and shape to the Milky Way. It also

⊙ *Viewing tip*

Around 2.5 million light years away from us, the Andromeda Galaxy is often described as the furthest object easily visible to the unaided eye. But it's not that easy to see – especially if you are suffering some light pollution. The trick is to memorize the star patterns in Andromeda and look slightly to the side of where you expect the galaxy to be. This technique – called 'averted vision' – causes the image to fall on parts of the retina that are more light-sensitive than the central region, which is designed to see fine detail.

hosts two bright companion galaxies – just like our Milky Way – as well as a flotilla of orbiting dwarf galaxies.

Unlike other galaxies, which are receding from us as a result of the expansion of the Universe, the Milky Way and Andromeda are approaching each other. It's estimated that they will merge in 5 billion years' time. The result of the collision may be a giant elliptical galaxy – Milkomeda – devoid of the gas that gives birth to stars, and dominated by ancient red giants.

## OCTOBER'S PICTURE

The **Triangulum Galaxy** (M33) may be the most distant object visible to the unaided eye. Observers in desert locations claim to have seen this sprawled-out spiral of some 40 billion stars in pitch-black skies. Any reports from the UK? At 3 million light years distant, M33 is the third-largest member of our Local Group of galaxies. Much smaller and more unformed than its neighbour spirals – Andromeda and the Milky Way – it is nevertheless a veritable hotbed of star formation.

## OCTOBER'S TOPIC
### Light pollution

We once received a letter from a lady in Kent, saying: 'Before the War, we could see so many stars. But they're not there any more. Have they faded?' No – light pollution is the culprit. Our skies are crammed with particles of dust, coming from sources like car exhausts and factory emissions. Couple this with badly-designed streetlighting, security lights and sports lighting – and, hey presto, the stars disappear. It's not just an aesthetic issue. It's calculated that Britain throws away £1 billion a year in badly-designed lighting.

It is robbing us of our vision of the skies – and contributing to global warming in emissions from coal-burning power stations. It isn't even making our lives any safer from crime, for research shows that more crimes are committed in well-lit areas. What's to be done? The Clean Neighbourhoods Act, which addresses (among other nuisances) noise and light pollution, should make a difference. And lighting engineers are actively working on new designs for street-lights that point the light down, and not up.

The good news is that two sites in the UK have been designated as 'dark sky sites', where people can enjoy our starlit skies again. One is Galloway Forest Park in Scotland. The other is diminutive Sark, in the Channel Islands – the world's first-ever Dark Sky Island!

Y ou know that winter is on its way as the beautiful **Pleiades** star cluster starts to climb in the eastern sky. 'A swarm of fireflies tangled in a silver braid' was the evocative description of the Pleiades by Alfred, Lord Tennyson, in his 1842 poem 'Locksley Hall'. All over the world, people have been intrigued by this lovely sight. From Greece to Australia, ancient myths independently describe the stars as a group of young girls being chased by an aggressive male – often **Aldebaran** or **Orion** – giving rise to the cluster's popular name, the Seven Sisters. Polynesian navigators used the Pleiades to mark the start of their year. And farmers in the Andes rely on the visibility of the Pleiades as a guide to planting their potatoes: the brightness or faintness of the Seven Sisters depends on El Niño, which affects the forthcoming weather.

### NOVEMBER'S CONSTELLATION

**Perseus** and its neighbour, **Cassiopeia**, are two of the best-loved constellations in the northern night sky. They never set as seen from Britain, and are packed with celestial goodies. In legend, Perseus is the superhero who slew Medusa, the Gorgon. The brightest star of the constellation is called **Mirfak** ('elbow' in Arabic) – a star nearly 600 light years away and 5000 times more luminous than our Sun.

But the 'star' of Perseus has to be **Algol** (whose name stems from the Arabic *al-Ghul* – the 'demon star'). It represents the eye of Medusa – and it winks. Its variations were first brought to the attention of the astronomical community by 18-year-old John Goodricke, a profoundly deaf amateur astronomer. He correctly surmised that the variations were caused by a fainter star eclipsing a brighter one (there are actually three stars in the system). Over a period of almost 2.9 days, the brightness of Algol varies between magnitude +2.1 to +3.4.

▼ The sky at 10 pm in mid-November, with Moon positions at three-day intervals either side of Full Moon. The star positions are also correct for 11 pm at

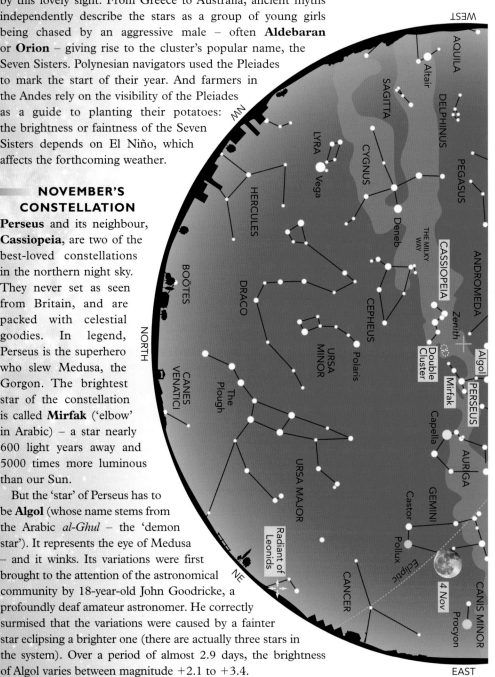

*the beginning of November, and 9 pm at the end of the month. The planets move slightly relative to the stars during the month.*

Another gem in Perseus – or to be exact, two of them – is the **Double Cluster**, h and chi Persei. The duo lies between Perseus and Cassiopeia, and is a sensational sight in binoculars. Some 7000 light years distant, the clusters are made of bright young blue stars – those in h are 5.6 million years old, while chi has only been around for a mere 3.2 million years (compare this to our Sun: it has notched up 4.6 billion years so far!).

## PLANETS ON VIEW

Mighty **Jupiter** lords it over the evening sky, and is now visible all night long in Taurus. At magnitude −2.6, the giant planet far outshines even the bright 'winter stars' of Orion and his neighbours. Use a small telescope – or even binoculars held steadily – to observe the four largest moons.

If you're keen to hunt out some fainter worlds, the evening sky has three on offer. Real **Mars**-worshippers are rejoicing, as the Red Planet – sunk into the twilight for a couple of months – makes a resurgence into darker skies at the end of November. But you'll need to look pretty closely low in the south-west, before the magnitude +1.2 planet sets at 5.50 pm.

Additional challenges include distant **Neptune**, shining at magnitude +7.9 in Aquarius and setting around 11.30 pm; and **Uranus** (magnitude +5.8), setting about 2.30 am in Pisces. There's more obvious action in the morning sky. **Venus** is brilliant at magnitude −3.9: it rises at 3.30 am at the beginning of November, but it's

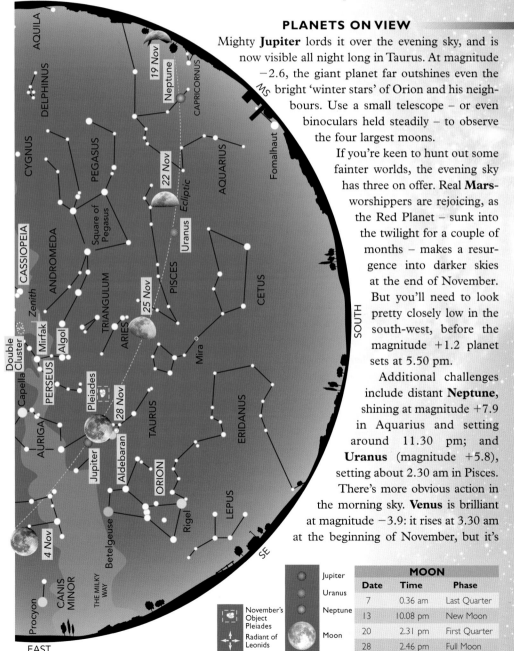

| MOON | | |
|---|---|---|
| **Date** | **Time** | **Phase** |
| 7 | 0.36 am | Last Quarter |
| 13 | 10.08 pm | New Moon |
| 20 | 2.31 pm | First Quarter |
| 28 | 2.46 pm | Full Moon |

gradually sinking and you'll have to wait until 5.00 am to see the Morning Star at the end of the month. On the morning of 17 November, Venus passes Spica; and it lies very close to Saturn on the morning of 27 November (see Special Events).

**Saturn** re-emerges from the Sun's glare in the morning sky in the middle of November. Lying in Virgo, the ringed planet shines at magnitude +0.9 and rises by 4.40 am at the close of November.

And, in the last few days of the month, you may catch **Mercury** (magnitude −0.1) to the lower left of Venus and Saturn, just above the south-eastern horizon before dawn.

## MOON

On 1 November, the Moon is close to Jupiter. The crescent Moon lies near Venus in the morning of 11 November. Back in the evening sky, you'll find the crescent Moon above Mars on 16 November. The Full Moon lies very close to Jupiter on 28 November, with Aldebaran below.

## SPECIAL EVENTS

There's a total eclipse of the Sun on **13 November**, though it's not visible from the UK. To see totality, you'll need to be in Queensland, Australia (where it's 14 November, local time), or on the narrow eclipse track across the South Pacific: the whole of this ocean region will witness a partial eclipse.

The night of **16/17 November** sees the maximum of the **Leonid** meteor shower. A few years ago, this annual shower yielded literally storms of shooting stars, but the rate has gone down as the parent comet Tempel-Tuttle, which sheds its dust to produce the meteors, has moved away from the vicinity of Earth. We have good observing conditions for the Leonids this year, as the Moon sets early.

In the morning skies of **27 November**, Venus and Saturn are just a degree apart – a striking sight for the naked eye or binoculars.

## NOVEMBER'S OBJECT

The **Pleiades** star cluster is one of the most familiar sky-sights. Though it's well known as the Seven Sisters, most people see any number of stars but seven! Most people can pick out the six brightest stars, while very keen-sighted observers can discern

### ◉ *Viewing tip*

Now that the nights are drawing in earlier, and becoming darker, it's a good time to pick out faint, fuzzy objects like the Andromeda Galaxy and the Orion Nebula. But don't even think about it near the time of Full Moon – its light will drown them out. The best time to observe 'deep-sky objects' is when the Moon is near to New, or well after Full Moon. Check the Moon phases timetable in the book.

up to 11 stars. These are just the most luminous in a group of 500 stars, lying about 400 light years away (although there's an ongoing debate about the precise distance!). The brightest stars in the Pleiades are hot and blue, and all the stars are young – less than 80 million years old. They were born together, and have yet to go their separate ways. The fledgling stars have blundered into a cloud of gas in space, which looks like gossamer on webcam images. Even to the unaided eye or through binoculars, they are still a beautiful sight.

## NOVEMBER'S PICTURE

If you're lucky enough to be in Queensland, Australia, on the morning of 14 November local time, this will be the sight that will greet your eyes. A **total eclipse of the Sun** is worth travelling the world for: nothing can prepare you for the magnificence of the spectacle, when our humble Moon exactly overlaps our magnificent Sun. This beautiful time-lapse image shows what treats are in store.

## NOVEMBER'S TOPIC
### Extrasolar planets

The tally of planets circling other stars now stands at over 500 – and more than 1000 wait to be confirmed.

The first came in 1995, when Swiss astronomers Michel Mayor and Didier Queloz discovered that the faint star 51 Pegasi – just to the right of the great Square of Pegasus – was being pulled backwards and forwards every four days. It had to be the work of a planet, tugging on its parent star. Astonishingly, this planet is around the same size as the Solar System's giant, Jupiter, but it is far closer to its star than Mercury. Astronomers call such planets 'hot jupiters'.

A team in California led by Geoff Marcy was already looking for planets, and soon found more. Now astronomers are finding whole solar systems with several worlds in stable orbits – like the six planets orbiting the star Gliese 581. One of these worlds is in the 'goldilocks zone' – possibly a rocky planet not much more massive than the Earth, which may harbour liquid water.

The latest breakthroughs are being made by NASA's Kepler orbiting spacecraft, which picks up tiny diminutions in light when a planet crosses the disc of its parent star. There are currently 1235 more candidates – 68 of them possible 'earths' – waiting to be checked out. Kepler researchers believe that the data they have garnered so far point to some 50 billion planets in the Galaxy.

The glorious constellations of winter are riding high in the sky. **Orion**, with his hunting dogs **Canis Major** and **Canis Minor**, is strutting his stuff across the heavens, fighting his adversary **Taurus** (the Bull). To add to the excitement, Taurus has an interloper this month. It's the brilliant planet Jupiter, visible in the south all month long. According to some historians, Jupiter may have been a candidate for the Christmas Star (see December's Topic).

▼ The sky at 10 pm in mid-December, with Moon positions at three-day intervals either side of Full Moon. The star positions are also correct for 11 pm at

### DECEMBER'S CONSTELLATION

Although **Taurus** is very much a second cousin to brilliant **Orion**, it is a fascinating constellation nonetheless. It's dominated by **Aldebaran** – the baleful blood-red eye of the celestial bull. Around 68 light years distant, and shining with a magnitude of +0.85, Aldebaran is a red giant star, but not one as extreme as neighbouring **Betelgeuse**. It is around three times heavier than the Sun. The 'head' of the bull is formed by the **Hyades** star cluster. The other famous star cluster in Taurus is the far more glamorous **Pleiades**, whose stars, although further away than the Hyades, are younger and brighter (see November's Object).

Taurus has two 'horns': the star **El Nath** (Arabic for 'the butting one') to the north, and **zeta Tauri** (whose Babylonian name Shurnarkabti-sha-shutu, meaning 'star in the bull towards the south', is thankfully not generally used!). Above this star is a stellar wreck – literally. In 1054, Chinese astronomers witnessed a brilliant 'new star' appear in this spot, which was visible in daytime for weeks. What the Chinese actually saw was an exploding star – a supernova – in its death throes. And today, we see its still-expanding remains as the **Crab Nebula**. It is visible through a medium-sized telescope (see December's Picture).

WEST

AQUARIUS

PEGASUS

Square of Pegasus

ANDROMEDA

PERSEUS

CYGNUS

THE MILKY WAY

CEPHEUS

Deneb

CASSIOPEIA

Capella

Zenith

AURIGA

GEMINI

Castor

Pollux

NW

LYRA

Vega

HERCULES

DRACO

Polaris

URSA MINOR

Radiant of Geminids

CANCER

Ecliptic

NORTH

BOÖTES

The Plough

URSA MAJOR

CANES VENATICI

NE

LEO

The Sickle

31 Dec

Regulus

EAST

*the beginning of December, and 9 pm at the end of the month. The planets move slightly relative to the stars during the month.*

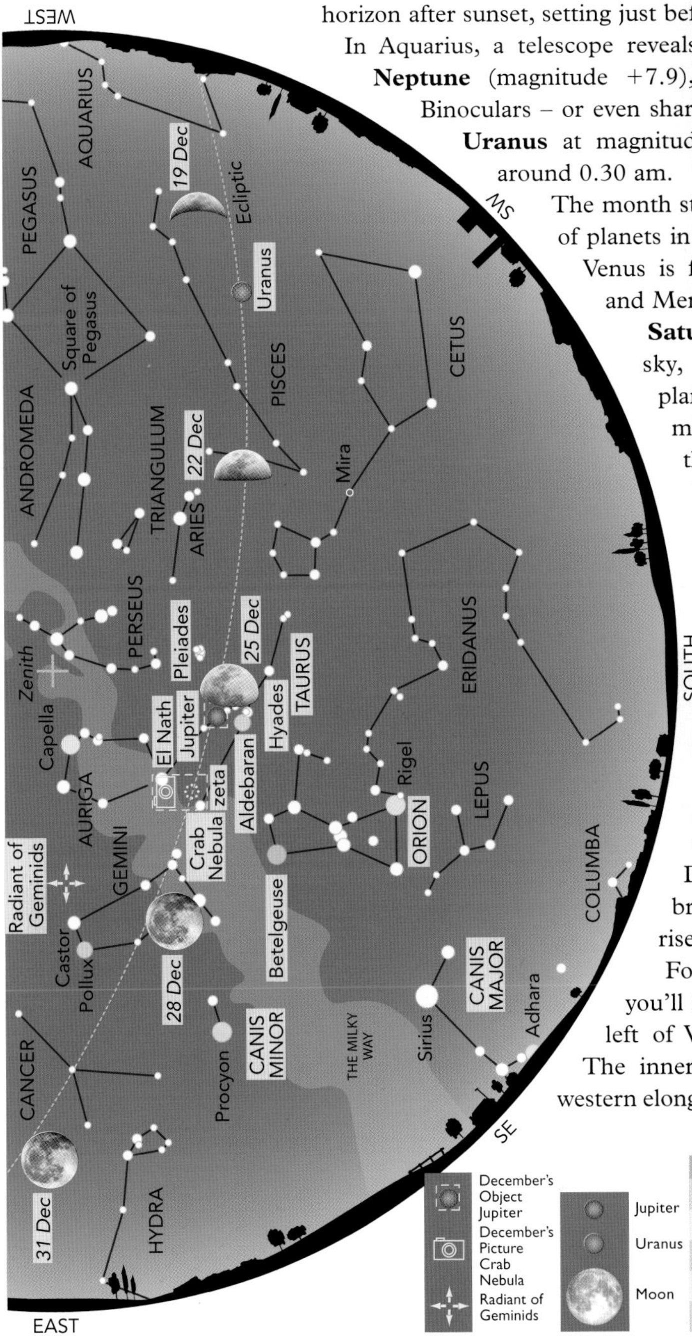

## PLANETS ON VIEW

This month, **Jupiter** reigns supreme. Visible all night long in Taurus, the giant planet is at opposition on 3 December (see December's Object). At magnitude −2.7, Jupiter lies above Aldebaran and the Hyades, with the Pleiades to its upper right.

**Mars** (magnitude +1.2) is skulking on the south-western horizon after sunset, setting just before 6.00 pm.

In Aquarius, a telescope reveals the most distant planet, **Neptune** (magnitude +7.9), setting about 9.30 pm. Binoculars – or even sharp eyesight – suffice to find **Uranus** at magnitude +5.8 in Pisces, setting around 0.30 am.

The month starts with a spectacular trio of planets in the pre-dawn sky: brilliant Venus is flanked by Saturn (above) and Mercury (below).

**Saturn** climbs steadily in the sky, leaving the other two planets behind. The ringworld moves from Virgo into Libra this month: at magnitude +0.9, it rises at 4.30 am at the beginning of December, and 3.00 am by the end of the month.

Brilliant **Venus** (magnitude −3.8) still dominates the morning sky, but it's slipping down towards the Sun. The Morning Star rises at 5.00 am when the month opens, but by the close of December the sky will be brightening by the time Venus rises at 6.30 am.

For the first half of December, you'll find **Mercury** to the lower left of Venus in the morning sky. The innermost planet is at greatest western elongation on 4 December, when

| | Jupiter |
| December's Object Jupiter | |
| December's Picture Crab Nebula | Uranus |
| Radiant of Geminids | Moon |

| MOON | | |
|---|---|---|
| **Date** | **Time** | **Phase** |
| 6 | 3.32 pm | Last Quarter |
| 13 | 8.42 am | New Moon |
| 20 | 5.19 am | First Quarter |
| 28 | 10.21 am | Full Moon |

*Star map labels (West to East):*

WEST — PEGASUS, AQUARIUS, Square of Pegasus, ANDROMEDA, TRIANGULUM, ARIES, PISCES, CETUS, Ecliptic, Uranus, 19 Dec, 22 Dec, 25 Dec, Mira, PERSEUS, Pleiades, El Nath, Jupiter, Hyades, TAURUS, Aldebaran, Crab Nebula zeta, Betelgeuse, ORION, Rigel, ERIDANUS, LEPUS, COLUMBA, Zenith, Capella, AURIGA, GEMINI, Castor, Pollux, CANCER, Radiant of Geminids, 28 Dec, 31 Dec, HYDRA, Procyon, CANIS MINOR, THE MILKY WAY, Sirius, CANIS MAJOR, Adhara, SOUTH, SE, SW, EAST

it rises at 5.50 am in the south-east and shines at magnitude −0.4.

### MOON

In the early hours of 9 December, the crescent Moon lies near Spica, and the following morning (10 December) the Moon is to the right of Saturn. Just before dawn on 11 December, look to the south-east to see the splendid spectacle of Venus with the crescent Moon and Mercury (see Special Events). In the evening sky, the crescent Moon lies above Mars on 15 December. On 25 December, the Moon lies close to giant planet Jupiter, with Aldebaran to the lower left.

### SPECIAL EVENTS

If you're up before dawn on **11 December**, look to the south-east around 6.30 am for a spectacular pairing of Venus with the crescent Moon; Mercury lies just to the lower left, with Saturn high up to the right.

The maximum of the **Geminid** meteor shower falls on **13/14 December**. These shooting stars are debris shed from an asteroid called Phaethon and therefore quite substantial – and hence bright. It's an excellent year for the Geminids, as the Moon is out of the way.

The Winter Solstice occurs at 11.12 am on **21 December**. As a result of the tilt of Earth's axis, the Sun reaches its lowest point in the heavens as seen from the northern hemisphere: we get the shortest days, and the longest nights.

### DECEMBER'S OBJECT

**Jupiter** is particularly bright this month. On 3 December, it's at opposition – meaning that it's opposite the Sun in the sky, and at its closest to the Earth. 'Close' is a relative term, however – the planet is still over 600 million kilometres away. But Jupiter is so vast (at 143,000 kilometres in diameter, it could contain 1300 Earths) and as it's made almost entirely of gas, it's very efficient at reflecting sunlight.

Although Jupiter is so huge, it spins faster than any other planet in the Solar System. It rotates every 9 hours 55 minutes, and as a result its equator bulges outwards – through a small telescope, it looks a bit like a tangerine crossed with an old-fashioned humbug. The humbug stripes are cloud belts of ammonia and methane stretched out by the planet's dizzy spin.

Jupiter has a fearsome magnetic field that no astronaut would survive, huge lightning storms, and an internal heat source

> **◉ Viewing tip**
>
> This is the month when you may be thinking of buying a telescope as a Christmas present for a budding stargazer. Beware! Unscrupulous mail-order catalogues selling 'gadgets' often advertise small telescopes that boast huge magnifications. This is known as 'empty magnification' – blowing up an image that the lens or mirror simply doesn't have the ability to get to grips with, so all you see is a bigger blur. A rule of thumb is to use a maximum magnification no greater than twice the diameter of your lens or mirror in millimetres. So if you have a 100 mm reflecting telescope, go no higher than 200×.

◀ *From a location near Hemel Hempstead, Hertfordshire, David Hepwood captured this image of the Crab Nebula. He used a 280 mm telescope and made three separate exposures through red, green and blue filters on an Atik 314L CCD camera.*

which means it radiates more energy than it receives from the Sun. Jupiter's core simmers at a temperature of 20,000°C.

Jupiter commands its own 'mini solar system' – a family of over 60 moons. The four biggest are visible in good binoculars, and even – to the really sharp-sighted – to the unaided eye. These are worlds in their own right – Ganymede is even bigger than the planet Mercury. But two vie for 'star' status: Io and Europa. The surface of Io is erupting with incredible geysers, sending plumes of sulphur dioxide 300 kilometres into space. Brilliant-white Europa probably contains oceans of liquid water beneath a solid ice coating, where alien fish may swim....

## DECEMBER'S PICTURE

Star-wreck: the **Crab Nebula**, in Taurus, is the remains of a star that was seen to explode in 1054. Its name comes from a description by the Irish astronomer Lord Rosse, who – in 1848 – compared its extremities to the pincers of a crab. Some 15 light years across, and still expanding, the Crab is home to the core of the dead star – a pulsar spinning 30 times per second.

## DECEMBER'S TOPIC
### The Christmas Star

Brilliant Jupiter, high in the sky this festive month, will focus attention as to the nature of the Christmas Star. What was the object that drew the Magi out of the East, and directed them to Bethlehem?

The answers are subtle, and possibly unanswerable, being rooted in the mists of antiquity and hearsay. First of all, we need to establish the date of the birth of Christ. It was certainly not AD 1, but a date somewhat before that, due to a counting error in the 6th century AD.

In 5 BC, Chinese astronomers reported a comet and/or a nova in the sky. But neither would account for the fact that King Herod couldn't see these celestial portents.

The key fact is that the Magi were astrologers. And in 7 BC, they worked out that the planets Jupiter and Saturn would draw together on three occasions to create a rare 'triple conjunction'. To astrologers, Jupiter was the king of the planets and Saturn the planet of the Jews. The message was clear: the King of the Jews was about to come into the world.

So there was no brilliant star. But taking together all the astronomical evidence, David Hughes – a world expert on the Christmas Star – reckons that the best-guess date for Christ's birth is 15 September 7 BC. An early excuse for a Christmas celebration!

There's always something to see in our Solar System, from planets to meteors or the Moon. These objects are very close to us – in astronomical terms – so their positions, shapes and sizes appear to change constantly. It is important to know when, where and how to look if you are to enjoy exploring Earth's neighbourhood. Here we give the best dates in 2012 for observing the planets and meteors (weather permitting!), and explain some of the concepts that will help you to get the most out of your observing.

## THE INFERIOR PLANETS

A planet with an orbit that lies closer to the Sun than the orbit of Earth is known as *inferior*. Mercury and Venus are the inferior planets. They show a full range of phases (like the Moon) from the thinnest crescents to full, depending on their position in relation to the Earth and the Sun. The diagram below shows the various positions of the inferior planets. They are invisible when at *conjunction*, when they are either behind the Sun, or between the Earth and the Sun, and lost in the latter's glare.

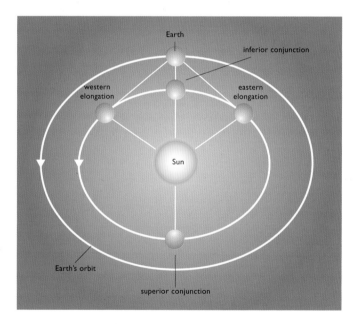

### Mercury

In the first week of January, Mercury is visible low in the south-east before dawn. It re-emerges at the end of February, very low in the west after sunset, and puts on its best evening show of the year in the first half of March. Mercury's best morning appearance runs from the last week of November to mid-December.

**Magnitudes**

Astronomers measure the brightness of stars, planets and other celestial objects using a scale of *magnitudes*. Somewhat confusingly, fainter objects have higher magnitudes, while brighter objects have lower magnitudes; the most brilliant stars have negative magnitudes! Naked-eye stars range from magnitude −1.5 for the brightest star, Sirius, to +6.5 for the faintest stars you can see on a really dark night.

As a guide, here are the magnitudes of selected objects:

| | |
|---|---|
| Sun | −26.7 |
| Full Moon | −12.5 |
| Venus (at its brightest) | −4.7 |
| Sirius | −1.5 |
| Betelgeuse | +0.4 |
| Polaris (Pole Star) | +2.0 |
| Faintest star visible to the naked eye | +6.5 |
| Faintest star visible to the Hubble Space Telescope | +31 |

◀ At eastern or western elongation, an inferior planet is at its maximum angular distance from the Sun. Conjunction occurs at two stages in the planet's orbit. Under certain circumstances, an inferior planet can transit across the Sun's disc at inferior conjunction.

| Maximum elongations of Mercury in 2012 | |
|---|---|
| Date | Separation |
| 5 March | 18° east |
| 18 April | 28° west |
| 1 July | 26° east |
| 16 August | 19° west |
| 26 October | 24° east |
| 4 December | 21° west |

| Maximum elongations of Venus in 2012 | |
|---|---|
| Date | Separation |
| 27 March | 46° east |
| 15 August | 46° west |

## Venus

From the beginning of the year, Venus is brilliant in the west as the Evening Star, reaching greatest eastern elongation on 27 March. It disappears from view by the end of May, to re-emerge as the Morning Star around the middle of June. Venus is then visible before dawn to the end of the year.

## THE SUPERIOR PLANETS

The superior planets are those with orbits that lie beyond that of the Earth. They are Mars, Jupiter, Saturn, Uranus and Neptune. The best time to observe a superior planet is when the Earth lies between it and the Sun. At this point in a planet's orbit, it is said to be at *opposition*.

▶ *Superior planets are invisible at conjunction. At quadrature the planet is at right angles to the Sun as viewed from Earth. Opposition is the best time to observe a superior planet.*

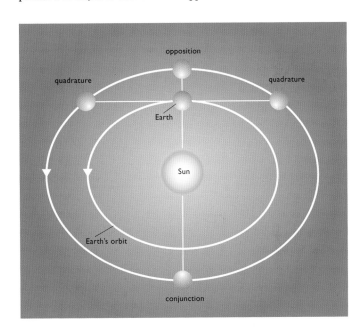

| Progress of Mars through the constellations | |
|---|---|
| January – mid-June | Leo |
| Mid-June – August | Virgo |
| September | Libra |
| First half of October | Scorpius |
| Mid-Oct – mid-Nov | Ophiuchus |
| Mid-Nov – end Dec | Sagittarius |

## Mars

The Red Planet brightens during January and February, until it reaches its two-yearly opposition on 3 March. Thereafter, it starts to fade until it is lost from view in October. It re-emerges from the Sun's glare at the end of November, low in the south-west in the early evening.

## Jupiter

Lying in Aries at the start of the year, Jupiter gradually fades until, by the end of April, it has disappeared into the Sun's glare. It reappears in the north-east in June, lying in Taurus, near the Pleiades. In the early morning of 15 July, Jupiter is occulted by the Moon. Brightening through the autumn months, the planet reaches opposition on 3 December.

### Saturn

Saturn is at its best for observing from January to August, reaching opposition on 15 April. By early September it has sunk into the twilight glow, but re-emerges in the morning in mid-November. After spending most of the year in Virgo, Saturn moves into Libra in December.

### Uranus

At the start of the year, Uranus is just visible to the naked eye, but by March it has disappeared into the twilight glow. It re-appears in June, and visibility improves into the autumn. Uranus is in Pisces all year, and reaches opposition on 29 September.

### Neptune

Neptune lies in Aquarius all year, and is best viewed from May onwards. It is at opposition on 24 August.

## SOLAR AND LUNAR ECLIPSES

### Solar Eclipses

There are two solar eclipses in 2012. The first, on 20/21 May, is an annular eclipse (where the Moon appears too small to cover the Sun's face completely), which can be seen in the North Pacific, from China and Japan to California and New Mexico; a partial eclipse is visible from Siberia and north-western North America. The second, a total eclipse, takes place on 13/14 November, and will be viewable only in Queensland, Australia, and on the narrow eclipse track across the South Pacific; the whole of this ocean region will see a partial eclipse.

### Lunar Eclipses

On 4 June there will be a partial eclipse of the Moon, visible only from the Pacific Ocean and the countries around it.

> **Astronomical distances**
> For objects in the Solar System, such as the planets, we can give their distances from the Earth in kilometres. But the distances are just too huge once we reach out to the stars. Even the nearest star (Proxima Centauri) lies 25 million million kilometres away.
> So astronomers use a larger unit – the *light year*. This is the distance that light travels in one year, and it equals 9.46 million million kilometres.
> Here are the distances to some familiar astronomical objects, in light years:
>
> | | |
> |---|---|
> | Proxima Centauri | 4.2 |
> | Betelgeuse | 640 |
> | Centre of the Milky Way | 27,000 |
> | Andromeda Galaxy | 2.5 million |
> | Most distant galaxies seen by the Hubble Space Telescope | 13 billion |

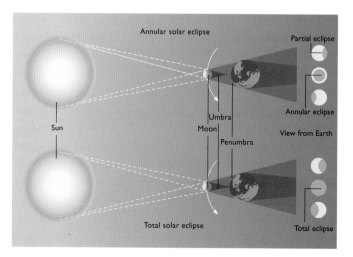

◄ *Where the dark central part (the umbra) of the Moon's shadow reaches the Earth, we see a total eclipse. People located within the penumbra see a partial eclipse. If the umbral shadow does not reach the Earth, we see an annular eclipse. This type of eclipse occurs when the Moon is at a distant point in its orbit and is not quite large enough to cover the whole of the Sun's disc.*

| Dates of maximum for selected meteor showers | |
|---|---|
| Meteor shower | Date of maximum |
| Quadrantids | 3/4 January |
| Lyrids | 21/22 April |
| Eta Aquarids | 4/5 May |
| Perseids | 12/13 August |
| Orionids | 20/21 October |
| Leonids | 16/17 November |
| Geminids | 13/14 December |

▶ *Meteors from a common source, occurring during a shower, enter the atmosphere along parallel trajectories. As a result of perspective, however, they appear to diverge from a single point in the sky – the radiant.*

## METEOR SHOWERS

Shooting stars – or *meteors* – are tiny particles of interplanetary dust, known as *meteoroids*, burning up in the Earth's atmosphere. At certain times of year, the Earth passes through a stream of these meteoroids (usually debris left behind by a comet) and we see a *meteor shower*. The point in the sky from which the meteors appear to emanate is known as the *radiant*. Most showers are known by the constellation in which the radiant is situated.

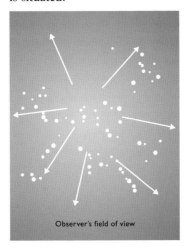
Observer's field of view

When watching meteors for a co-ordinated meteor programme, observers generally note the time, seeing conditions, cloud cover, their own location, the time and brightness of each meteor, and whether it was from the main meteor stream. It is also worth noting details of persistent afterglows (trains) and fireballs, and making counts of how many meteors appear in a given period.

### Angular separations

Astronomers measure the distance between objects, as we see them in the sky, by the angle between the objects in degrees (symbol °). From the horizon to the point above your head is 90 degrees. All around the horizon is 360 degrees.

You can use your hand, held at arm's length, as a rough guide to angular distances, as follows:
Width of index finger 1°
Width of clenched hand 10°
Thumb to little finger
on outspread hand 20°
For smaller distances, astronomers divide the degree into 60 arcminutes (symbol ′), and the arcminute into 60 arcseconds (symbol ″).

## COMETS

Comets are small bodies in orbit about the Sun. Consisting of frozen gases and dust, they are often known as 'dirty snowballs'. When their orbits bring them close to the Sun, the ices evaporate and dramatic tails of gas and dust can sometimes be seen.

A number of comets move round the Sun in fairly small, elliptical orbits in periods of a few years; others have much longer periods. Most really brilliant comets have orbital periods of several thousands or even millions of years. The exception is Comet Halley, a bright comet with a period of about 76 years. It was last seen with the naked eye in 1986.

Binoculars and wide-field telescopes provide the best views of comet tails. Larger telescopes with a high magnification are necessary to observe fine detail in the gaseous head (*coma*). Most comets are discovered with professional instruments, but a few are still found by experienced amateur astronomers.

None of the known comets is predicted to reach naked-eye brightness in 2012, but there's always a chance of a bright new comet putting in a surprise appearance.

Deep-sky objects are 'fuzzy patches' that lie outside the Solar System. They include star clusters, nebulae and galaxies. To observe the majority of deep-sky objects you will need binoculars or a telescope, but there are also some beautiful naked-eye objects, notably the Pleiades and the Orion Nebula.

The faintest object that an instrument can see is its *limiting magnitude*. The table gives a rough guide, for good seeing conditions, for a variety of small- to medium-sized telescopes.

We have provided a selection of recommended deep-sky targets, together with their magnitudes. Some are described in more detail in our monthly 'Object' features. Look on the appropriate month's map to find which constellations are on view, and then choose your objects using the list below. We have provided celestial coordinates for readers with detailed star maps. The suggested times of year for viewing are when the constellation is highest in the sky in the late evening.

| Limiting magnitude for small to medium telescopes | |
|---|---|
| Aperture (mm) | Limiting magnitude |
| 50 | +11.2 |
| 60 | +11.6 |
| 70 | +11.9 |
| 80 | +12.2 |
| 100 | +12.7 |
| 125 | +13.2 |
| 150 | +13.6 |

## RECOMMENDED DEEP-SKY OBJECTS

**Andromeda** – autumn and early winter

| | |
|---|---|
| M31 (NGC 224) Andromeda Galaxy | 3rd-magnitude spiral galaxy RA 00h 42.7m Dec +41° 16' |
| M32 (NGC 221) | 8th-magnitude elliptical galaxy, a companion to M31 RA 00h 42.7m Dec +40° 52' |
| M110 (NGC 205) | 8th-magnitude elliptical galaxy RA 00h 40.4m Dec +41° 41' |
| NGC 7662 Blue Snowball | 8th-magnitude planetary nebula RA 23h 25.9m Dec +42° 33' |

**Aquarius** – late autumn and early winter

| | |
|---|---|
| M2 (NGC 7089) | 6th-magnitude globular cluster RA 21h 33.5m Dec –00° 49' |
| M72 (NGC 6981) | 9th-magnitude globular cluster RA 20h 53.5m Dec –12° 32' |
| NGC 7293 Helix Nebula | 7th-magnitude planetary nebula RA 22h 29.6m Dec –20° 48' |
| NGC 7009 Saturn Nebula | 8th-magnitude planetary nebula RA 21h 04.2m Dec –11° 22' |

**Aries** – early winter

| | |
|---|---|
| NGC 772 | 10th-magnitude spiral galaxy RA 01h 59.3m Dec +19° 01' |

**Auriga** – winter

| | |
|---|---|
| M36 (NGC 1960) | 6th-magnitude open cluster RA 05h 36.1m Dec +34° 08' |
| M37 (NGC 2099) | 6th-magnitude open cluster RA 05h 52.4m Dec +32° 33' |
| M38 (NGC 1912) | 6th-magnitude open cluster RA 05h 28.7m Dec +35° 50' |

**Cancer** – late winter to early spring

| | |
|---|---|
| M44 (NGC 2632) Praesepe or Beehive | 3rd-magnitude open cluster RA 08h 40.1m Dec +19° 59' |
| M67 (NGC 2682) | 7th-magnitude open cluster RA 08h 50.4m Dec +11° 49' |

**Canes Venatici** – visible all year

| | |
|---|---|
| M3 (NGC 5272) | 6th-magnitude globular cluster RA 13h 42.2m Dec +28° 23' |

| | |
|---|---|
| M51 (NGC 5194/5) Whirlpool Galaxy | 8th-magnitude spiral galaxy RA 13h 29.9m Dec +47° 12' |
| M63 (NGC 5055) | 9th-magnitude spiral galaxy RA 13h 15.8m Dec +42° 02' |
| M94 (NGC 4736) | 8th-magnitude spiral galaxy RA 12h 50.9m Dec +41° 07' |
| M106 (NGC4258) | 8th-magnitude spiral galaxy RA 12h 19.0m Dec +47° 18' |

**Canis Major** – late winter

| | |
|---|---|
| M41 (NGC 2287) | 4th-magnitude open cluster RA 06h 47.0m Dec –20° 44' |

**Capricornus** – late summer and early autumn

| | |
|---|---|
| M30 (NGC 7099) | 7th-magnitude globular cluster RA 21h 40.4m Dec –23° 11' |

**Cassiopeia** – visible all year

| | |
|---|---|
| M52 (NGC 7654) | 6th-magnitude open cluster RA 23h 24.2m Dec +61° 35' |
| M103 (NGC 581) | 7th-magnitude open cluster RA 01h 33.2m Dec +60° 42' |
| NGC 225 | 7th-magnitude open cluster RA 00h 43.4m Dec +61 47' |
| NGC 457 | 6th-magnitude open cluster RA 01h 19.1m Dec +58° 20' |
| NGC 663 | Good binocular open cluster RA 01h 46.0m Dec +61° 15' |

**Cepheus** – visible all year

| | |
|---|---|
| Delta Cephei | Variable star, varying between +3.5 and +4.4 with a period of 5.37 days. It has a magnitude +6.3 companion and they make an attractive pair for small telescopes or binoculars. |

**Cetus** – late autumn

| | |
|---|---|
| Mira (omicron Ceti) | Irregular variable star with a period of roughly 330 days and a range between +2.0 and +10.1. |
| M77 (NGC 1068) | 9th-magnitude spiral galaxy RA 02h 42.7m Dec –00° 01' |

**Coma Berenices** – spring

| | |
|---|---|
| M53 (NGC 5024) | 8th-magnitude globular cluster<br>RA 13h 12.9m Dec +18° 10' |
| M64 (NGC 4286)<br>Black Eye Galaxy | 8th-magnitude spiral galaxy with<br>a prominent dust lane that is<br>visible in larger telescopes.<br>RA 12h 56.7m Dec +21° 41' |
| M85 (NGC 4382) | 9th-magnitude elliptical galaxy<br>RA 12h 25.4m Dec +18° 11' |
| M88 (NGC 4501) | 10th-magnitude spiral galaxy<br>RA 12h 32.0m Dec.+14° 25' |
| M91 (NGC 4548) | 10th-magnitude spiral galaxy<br>RA 12h 35.4m Dec +14° 30' |
| M98 (NGC 4192) | 10th-magnitude spiral galaxy<br>RA 12h 13.8m Dec +14° 54' |
| M99 (NGC 4254) | 10th-magnitude spiral galaxy<br>RA 12h 18.8m Dec +14° 25' |
| M100 (NGC 4321) | 9th-magnitude spiral galaxy<br>RA 12h 22.9m Dec +15° 49' |
| NGC 4565 | 10th-magnitude spiral galaxy<br>RA 12h 36.3m Dec +25° 59' |

**Cygnus** – late summer and autumn

| | |
|---|---|
| Cygnus Rift | Dark cloud just south of Deneb<br>that appears to split the Milky<br>Way in two. |
| NGC 7000<br>North America Nebula | A bright nebula against the back-<br>ground of the Milky Way, visible<br>with binoculars under dark skies.<br>RA 20h 58.8m Dec +44° 20' |
| NGC 6992<br>Veil Nebula (part) | Supernova remnant, visible with<br>binoculars under dark skies.<br>RA 20h 56.8m Dec +31 28' |
| M29 (NGC 6913) | 7th-magnitude open cluster<br>RA 20h 23.9m Dec +36° 32' |
| M39 (NGC 7092) | Large 5th-magnitude open cluster<br>RA 21h 32.2m Dec +48° 26' |
| NGC 6826<br>Blinking Planetary | 9th-magnitude planetary nebula<br>RA 19 44.8m Dec +50° 31' |

**Delphinus** – late summer

| | |
|---|---|
| NGC 6934 | 9th-magnitude globular cluster<br>RA 20h 34.2m Dec +07° 24' |

**Draco** – midsummer

| | |
|---|---|
| NGC 6543 | 9th-magnitude planetary nebula<br>RA 17h 58.6m Dec +66° 38' |

**Gemini** – winter

| | |
|---|---|
| M35 (NGC 2168) | 5th-magnitude open cluster<br>RA 06h 08.9m Dec +24° 20' |
| NGC 2392<br>Eskimo Nebula | 8–10th-magnitude planetary nebula<br>RA 07h 29.2m Dec +20° 55' |

**Hercules** – early summer

| | |
|---|---|
| M13 (NGC 6205) | 6th-magnitude globular cluster<br>RA 16h 41.7m Dec +36° 28' |
| M92 (NGC 6341) | 6th-magnitude globular cluster<br>RA 17h 17.1m Dec +43° 08' |
| NGC 6210 | 9th-magnitude planetary nebula<br>RA 16h 44.5m Dec +23 49' |

**Hydra** – early spring

| | |
|---|---|
| M48 (NGC 2548) | 6th-magnitude open cluster<br>RA 08h 13.8m Dec –05° 48' |
| M68 (NGC 4590) | 8th-magnitude globular cluster<br>RA 12h 39.5m Dec –26° 45' |

| | |
|---|---|
| M83 (NGC 5236) | 8th-magnitude spiral galaxy<br>RA 13h 37.0m Dec –29° 52' |
| NGC 3242<br>Ghost of Jupiter | 9th-magnitude planetary nebula<br>RA 10h 24.8m Dec –18°38' |

**Leo** – spring

| | |
|---|---|
| M65 (NGC 3623) | 9th-magnitude spiral galaxy<br>RA 11h 18.9m Dec +13° 05' |
| M66 (NGC 3627) | 9th-magnitude spiral galaxy<br>RA 11h 20.2m Dec +12° 59' |
| M95 (NGC 3351) | 10th-magnitude spiral galaxy<br>RA 10h 44.0m Dec +11° 42' |
| M96 (NGC 3368) | 9th-magnitude spiral galaxy<br>RA 10h 46.8m Dec +11° 49' |
| M105 (NGC 3379) | 9th-magnitude elliptical galaxy<br>RA 10h 47.8m Dec +12° 35' |

**Lepus** – winter

| | |
|---|---|
| M79 (NGC 1904) | 8th-magnitude globular cluster<br>RA 05h 24.5m Dec –24° 33' |

**Lyra** – spring

| | |
|---|---|
| M56 (NGC 6779) | 8th-magnitude globular cluster<br>RA 19h 16.6m Dec +30° 11' |
| M57 (NGC 6720)<br>Ring Nebula | 9th-magnitude planetary nebula<br>RA 18h 53.6m Dec +33° 02' |

**Monoceros** – winter

| | |
|---|---|
| M50 (NGC 2323) | 6th-magnitude open cluster<br>RA 07h 03.2m Dec –08° 20' |
| NGC 2244 | Open cluster surrounded by the<br>faint Rosette Nebula, NGC 2237.<br>Visible in binoculars.<br>RA 06h 32.4m Dec +04° 52' |

**Ophiuchus** – summer

| | |
|---|---|
| M9 (NGC 6333) | 8th-magnitude globular cluster<br>RA 17h 19.2m Dec –18° 31' |
| M10 (NGC 6254) | 7th-magnitude globular cluster<br>RA 16h 57.1m Dec –04° 06' |
| M12 (NCG 6218) | 7th-magnitude globular cluster<br>RA 16h 47.2m Dec –01° 57' |
| M14 (NGC 6402) | 8th-magnitude globular cluster<br>RA 17h 37.6m Dec –03° 15' |
| M19 (NGC 6273) | 7th-magnitude globular cluster<br>RA 17h 02.6m Dec –26° 16' |
| M62 (NGC 6266) | 7th-magnitude globular cluster<br>RA 17h 01.2m Dec –30° 07' |
| M107 (NGC 6171) | 8th-magnitude globular cluster<br>RA 16h 32.5m Dec –13° 03' |

**Orion** – winter

| | |
|---|---|
| M42 (NGC 1976)<br>Orion Nebula | 4th-magnitude nebula<br>RA 05h 35.4m Dec –05° 27' |
| M43 (NGC 1982) | 5th-magnitude nebula<br>RA 05h 35.6m Dec –05° 16' |
| M78 (NGC 2068) | 8th-magnitude nebula<br>RA 05h 46.7m Dec +00° 03' |

**Pegasus** – autumn

| | |
|---|---|
| M15 (NGC 7078) | 6th-magnitude globular cluster<br>RA 21h 30.0m Dec +12° 10' |

**Perseus** – autumn to winter

| | |
|---|---|
| M34 (NGC 1039) | 5th-magnitude open cluster<br>RA 02h 42.0m Dec +42° 47' |
| M76 (NGC 650/1)<br>Little Dumbbell | 11th-magnitude planetary nebula<br>RA 01h 42.4m Dec +51° 34' |

| | |
|---|---|
| NGC 869/884<br>Double Cluster | Pair of open star clusters<br>RA 02h 19.0m Dec +57° 09'<br>RA 02h 22.4m Dec +57° 07' |

**Pisces** – autumn

| | |
|---|---|
| M74 (NGC 628) | 9th-magnitude spiral galaxy<br>RA 01h 36.7m Dec +15° 47' |

**Puppis** – late winter

| | |
|---|---|
| M46 (NGC 2437) | 6th-magnitude open cluster<br>RA 07h 41.8m Dec −14° 49' |
| M47 (NGC 2422) | 4th-magnitude open cluster<br>RA 07h 36.6m Dec −14° 30' |
| M93 (NGC 2447) | 6th-magnitude open cluster<br>RA 07h 44.6m Dec −23° 52' |

**Sagitta** – late summer

| | |
|---|---|
| M71 (NGC 6838) | 8th-magnitude globular cluster<br>RA 19h 53.8m Dec +18° 47' |

**Sagittarius** – summer

| | |
|---|---|
| M8 (NGC 6523)<br>Lagoon Nebula | 6th-magnitude nebula<br>RA 18h 03.8m Dec −24° 23' |
| M17 (NGC 6618)<br>Omega Nebula | 6th-magnitude nebula<br>RA 18h 20.8m Dec −16° 11' |
| M18 (NGC 6613) | 7th-magnitude open cluster<br>RA 18h 19.9m Dec −17 08' |
| M20 (NGC 6514)<br>Trifid Nebula | 9th-magnitude nebula<br>RA 18h 02.3m Dec −23° 02' |
| M21 (NGC 6531) | 6th-magnitude open cluster<br>RA 18h 04.6m Dec −22° 30' |
| M22 (NGC 6656) | 5th-magnitude globular cluster<br>RA 18h 36.4m Dec −23° 54' |
| M23 (NGC 6494) | 5th-magnitude open cluster<br>RA 17h 56.8m Dec −19° 01' |
| M24 (NGC 6603) | 5th-magnitude open cluster<br>RA 18h 16.9m Dec −18° 29' |
| M25 (IC 4725) | 5th-magnitude open cluster<br>RA 18h 31.6m Dec −19° 15' |
| M28 (NGC 6626) | 7th-magnitude globular cluster<br>RA 18h 24.5m Dec −24° 52' |
| M54 (NGC 6715) | 8th-magnitude globular cluster<br>RA 18h 55.1m Dec −30° 29' |
| M55 (NGC 6809) | 7th-magnitude globular cluster<br>RA 19h 40.0m Dec −30° 58' |
| M69 (NGC 6637) | 8th-magnitude globular cluster<br>RA 18h 31.4m Dec −32° 21' |
| M70 (NGC 6681) | 8th-magnitude globular cluster<br>RA 18h 43.2m Dec −32° 18' |
| M75 (NGC 6864) | 9th-magnitude globular cluster<br>RA 20h 06.1m Dec −21° 55' |

**Scorpius (northern part)** – midsummer

| | |
|---|---|
| M4 (NGC 6121) | 6th-magnitude globular cluster<br>RA 16h 23.6m Dec −26° 32' |
| M7 (NGC 6475) | 3rd-magnitude open cluster<br>RA 17h 53.9m Dec −34° 49' |
| M80 (NGC 6093) | 7th-magnitude globular cluster<br>RA 16h 17.0m Dec −22° 59' |

**Scutum** – mid to late summer

| | |
|---|---|
| M11 (NGC 6705)<br>Wild Duck Cluster | 6th-magnitude open cluster<br>RA 18h 51.1m Dec −06° 16' |

| | |
|---|---|
| M26 (NGC 6694) | 8th-magnitude open cluster<br>RA 18h 45.2m Dec −09° 24' |

**Serpens** – summer

| | |
|---|---|
| M5 (NGC 5904) | 6th-magnitude globular cluster<br>RA 15h 18.6m Dec +02° 05' |
| M16 (NGC 6611) | 6th-magnitude open cluster,<br>surrounded by the Eagle Nebula.<br>RA 18h 18.8m Dec −13° 47' |

**Taurus** – winter

| | |
|---|---|
| M1 (NGC 1952)<br>Crab Nebula | 8th-magnitude supernova remnant<br>RA 05h 34.5m Dec +22° 00' |
| M45<br>Pleiades | 1st-magnitude open cluster,<br>an excellent binocular object.<br>RA 03h 47.0m Dec +24° 07' |

**Triangulum** – autumn

| | |
|---|---|
| M33 (NGC 598) | 6th-magnitude spiral galaxy<br>RA 01h 33.9m Dec +30° 39' |

**Ursa Major** – all year

| | |
|---|---|
| M81 (NGC 3031) | 7th-magnitude spiral galaxy<br>RA 09h 55.6m Dec +69° 04' |
| M82 (NGC 3034) | 8th-magnitude starburst galaxy<br>RA 09h 55.8m Dec +69° 41' |
| M97 (NGC 3587)<br>Owl Nebula | 12th-magnitude planetary nebula<br>RA 11h 14.8m Dec +55° 01' |
| M101 (NGC 5457) | 8th-magnitude spiral galaxy<br>RA 14h 03.2m Dec +54° 21' |
| M108 (NGC 3556) | 10th-magnitude spiral galaxy<br>RA 11h 11.5m Dec +55° 40' |
| M109 (NGC 3992) | 10th-magnitude spiral galaxy<br>RA 11h 57.6m Dec +53° 23' |

**Virgo** – spring

| | |
|---|---|
| M49 (NGC 4472) | 8th-magnitude elliptical galaxy<br>RA 12h 29.8m Dec +08° 00' |
| M58 (NGC 4579) | 10th-magnitude spiral galaxy<br>RA 12h 37.7m Dec +11° 49' |
| M59 (NGC 4621) | 10th-magnitude elliptical galaxy<br>RA 12h 42.0m Dec +11° 39' |
| M60 (NGC 4649) | 9th-magnitude elliptical galaxy<br>RA 12h 43.7m Dec +11° 33' |
| M61 (NGC 4303) | 10th-magnitude spiral galaxy<br>RA 12h 21.9m Dec +04° 28' |
| M84 (NGC 4374) | 9th-magnitude elliptical galaxy<br>RA 12h 25.1m Dec +12° 53' |
| M86 (NGC 4406) | 9th-magnitude elliptical galaxy<br>RA 12h 26.2m Dec +12° 57' |
| M87 (NGC 4486) | 9th-magnitude elliptical galaxy<br>RA 12h 30.8m Dec +12° 24' |
| M89 (NGC 4552) | 10th-magnitude elliptical galaxy<br>RA 12h 35.7m Dec +12° 33' |
| M90 (NGC 4569) | 9th-magnitude spiral galaxy<br>RA 12h 36.8m Dec +13° 10' |
| M104 (NGC 4594)<br>Sombrero Galaxy | Almost edge-on 8th-magnitude<br>spiral galaxy.<br>RA 12h 40.0m Dec −11° 37' |

**Vulpecula** – late summer and autumn

| | |
|---|---|
| M27 (NGC 6853)<br>Dumbbell Nebula | 8th-magnitude planetary nebula<br>RA 19h 59.6m Dec +22° 43' |

Observing the Sun has many advantages over other aspects of amateur astronomy – light pollution doesn't matter, you can avoid anti-social hours, and the Sun usually presents something new every time you observe it. For basic observing, even cheap and easily portable instruments are often perfectly adequate – because the Sun is bright, you don't need a large telescope. However, these days there's another side to solar observing, and it's one at the opposite extreme of cost.

Astronomy is a pretty safe hobby, but observing the Sun can be the exception. An inadvertent glance at the Sun through even the smallest telescope can cost you the sight of an eye, or at least leave you with permanent eye damage. So you need to take the right precautions. Until fairly recently, the approved safe way was to project the Sun's image. But now, this is less often recommended, and is even regarded as potentially dangerous.

To project the Sun's image, you simply line the telescope up on the Sun, use a low-magnification eyepiece and hold a screen, such as a piece of white card, behind the eyepiece so that the image of the Sun shines on to it. This image is safe to view, and has the advantage that several people can view it at once. So where's the danger?

One risk is that someone – a child maybe – may decide to take a quick peek through the eyepiece or even the finder, while the telescope is unattended. This doesn't apply if you are the only person around, and it's best to keep a cap on the finder in any case. The other risk is to your telescope. Many budget telescopes these days use plastic barrels for the eyepieces and their internal fittings. The Sun's heat can easily burn holes in the plastic, just as a magnifying glass will set fire to a piece of paper. Even with a more robust eyepiece, the heat can damage the resin between the glass elements. So again, if you use a simple type of eyepiece but with a metal casing, you can still project the Sun's image perfectly well, and this remains a perfectly acceptable means of solar observing as long as you are aware of the potential for damage.

▼ *A small telescope can be used to project the Sun's image, but cover the finder in case of accidents.*

### FULL-APERTURE FILTERS

An alternative way to observe the Sun safely is to reduce its power before the light even enters the telescope, using what's called a full-aperture filter, so there is no danger of anything overheating. The light must cut down by a factor of around 100,000, so these need to be made of the correct material – any old piece of dark

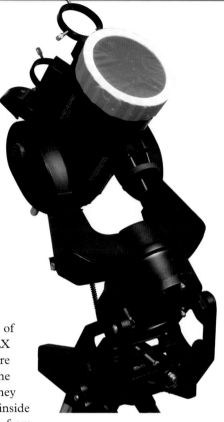

▶ *This Schmidt-Cassegrain telescope has been converted into a solar telescope using a home-made cap carrying inexpensive Baader AstroSolar filter material.*

glass or film won't do. However, they must be well secured so that there's no risk of them coming loose, such as when sticky tape loses its grip in the heat, and they must be free of any damage.

At one time, most small refracting telescopes were actually supplied with small Sun filters that you were meant to screw into the eyepiece when observing the Sun. The problem was that all the Sun's heat was concentrated on to this little piece of glass, which could shatter without warning. These were outlawed years ago and are now rarely seen, but if you come across one, don't use it.

Some manufacturers make filters for the front of specific telescopes, such as Meade ETX and LX instruments. These have the advantage that they are perfectly safe, as they are generally screwed into the filter thread at the top of the telescope tube, and they are made of glass with the filter coating on the inside where it is safe from being scratched. The filter from Telescope House for an ETX-125 costs around £70.

In many cases no such filter is available for your telescope, so you will have to make your own. Fortunately, this is a fairly simple matter, because you can buy the actual filtering material in sheets of coated Mylar. The most popular such material is Baader AstroSolar film, available in A4 sheets at reasonable prices – £15 from Green Witch, for example, who also supply it in larger sizes.

How you fix the material to the top of your telescope is up to you, but it must be secure and it must also be kept free of damage. Any creases can give rise to pinholes, which will render it unsafe. A cardboard cap is one possibility, or you can secure it to the inside of the existing tube cover if this has a removable cap about 40 mm diameter which is intended for solar observing by projection. You don't need to stretch it taut to keep it free of slight wrinkles, however – the material is very thin so these won't interfere with the image quality.

▼ *A white-light view of the Sun as seen through a 106 mm refractor equipped with Baader AstroSolar filter, taken on 28 October 2003.*

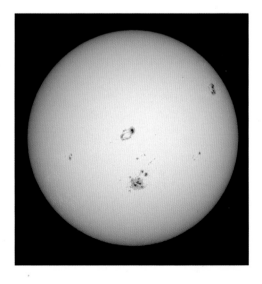

### SUPPLIERS OF THE EQUIPMENT MENTIONED HERE

Most equipment is available from a range of dealers in the UK.

Baader AstroSolar film – available from many suppliers including Green Witch: www.green-witch.com

Coronado solar telescopes from Telescope House: www.telescopehouse.com

Lunt solar telescopes: check www.luntsolarsystems.com for dealers

Solarscope/Solarview: check www.solarscope.co.uk

Daystar filters: check www.daystarfilters.com

*Prices quoted here are current as of mid-2011.*

AstroSolar film and many of the full-aperture filters give a neutral colour to the Sun, making it appear white, which is indeed its true colour. The popular belief that the Sun is yellow is a myth, because the only time we ever see its disc in the sky it is very much dimmed by cloud or by the atmosphere when low down. However, many people would prefer to see it looking yellow or orange, and some filters are tinted to make it this colour.

However, all such filters give what is essentially a white-light or continuum view, showing a wide range of wavelengths of the Sun's light. Using them you can view such phenomena as sunspots, faculae and limb darkening. You can watch the steady march of sunspots across the Sun's disc over a period of a week or so as the Sun rotates, and if you are lucky spot a rare white-light flare – a sudden bright eruption from within an active area of spots. But another myth is that flares are spectacular flame-like structures at the edge of the Sun's disc. These are actually called prominences, and they are far too faint to be seen under normal circumstances. To see those, you need a telescope equipped with a narrow-band filter.

### NARROW-BAND FILTERS

Rather than viewing the Sun in all wavelengths of light, narrow-band filters show just the light from specific atoms or molecules. This transforms the view of the Sun, and the deep red light of hydrogen atoms in particular (at a wavelength known as hydrogen alpha) is especially interesting. Prominences now become visible, as well as much greater detail on the surface. Sunspots, however, are less obvious, though you can usually tell where they are because of bright areas surrounding them.

But while the telescopes remain small, the cost of observing skyrockets because the filters are very expensive. The entry level instrument is the Coronado PST – standing for Personal Solar Telescope – and even this costs nearly £500 for the telescope alone. Even so, it is a very popular instrument, though it does have its drawbacks. Your first view through a PST may be a bit disappointing. Those prominences you have looked forward to seeing may not be immediately obvious, and the mottling of the solar surface is less dramatic than in photos,

▼ *A standard Coronado PST in use, attached to an equatorial mount. It has a camera thread, so you can also use an ordinary photographic tripod.*

where the contrast is enhanced. You may also need to constantly retune the filter (by turning a tube ring) to view either the prominences or the surface detail, as there is a 'sweet spot' which favours a limited area at a time. Furthermore, you can't just fit a camera to the instrument as you can with most telescopes because of the small focusing range.

The PST does allow you to view the Sun's changing narrow-band appearance very quickly and easily, hence its popularity. But once hooked, you may want to progress to something more costly still. The crucial figure is the bandpass. A basic PST filter has a bandpass of 1.0 Ångstroms (0.1 nanometres), while Lunt Solar Systems make a similarly priced instrument, the LS35 Tha, with a 0.75 Å bandpass.

In general, the smaller the bandpass, the better the view and the more you are likely to see at a single glance. You can get a more expensive PST with two filters (known as double-stacked) giving a bandpass of 0.5Å, and Lunt have a well-regarded instrument, the LS60 Tha, which has the added advantage of allowing photography.

*▲ A Lunt LS60 solar telescope gives good eyepiece views of details at the hydrogen-alpha wavelength, and can also be used for photography.*

But from there on, the costs increase drastically with both telescope aperture and filter bandpass. You can also purchase filter sets for specific telescopes up to 100 mm aperture. In this case, there is usually a full-aperture energy rejection filter which serves to reduce the amount of light and heat passing through the telescope, plus the all-important etalon which does the hard work of filtering the light down to a narrow waveband and which fits at the eyepiece end. As well as Coronado and Lunt, manufacturers of more advanced systems include Solarscope in the Isle of Man, Baader in Germany and Daystar in the United States.

*▼ Comparison of a white-light image of a sunspot and the same area seen through a double-stacked solar telescope on 8 March 2011. A brief flare on the solar surface has produced a prominence at the edge of the Sun. The images were recorded in monochrome and colorized afterwards.*

The costs of these systems rapidly become equivalent not just to a used car but to a new car. For example, a Solarview double-pass 70 mm filter system would set you back £10,000. But there are many devotees of this branch of astronomy who are prepared to pay such prices to view just one astronomical object – our ever-changing Sun.

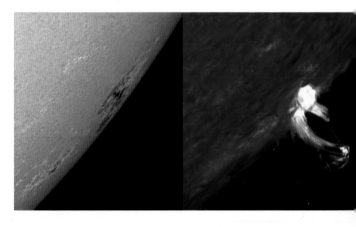